GUIDE

TO UNDERSTANDING

COMPLEX POST TRAUMATIC STRESS DISORDER

(C-PTSD)

Keys to Living a Healthier Lifestyle
Self-Care is Self-Love
Investing in your well-being is Fostering Self Love

MOREEN JORDAN, M.A., L.P.C.

ISBN: 978-0-692-18178-2

Printed in the United State of America

First Edition 2021

First Printing 2021

GUIDE

TO UNDERSTANDING

COMPLEX POST TRAUMATIC STRESS DISORDER

(C-PTSD)

ACKNOWLEDGMENTS

This book is dedicated to my mother (Faustine Vaughn) and son's: Emmanuel Jr. & Nicholas. For these three individuals have positively impacted my life in ways I will never be able to fully express or explain and for that I am eternally grateful. My mother was a woman who was wise before her times. Becoming a mother at the age of 18, she was a woman who had an unbelievable understanding of the importance of pouring love & safety into her children while creating safe places, emotional strength, and unyielding love in order to provide her family/children with opportunities for happy and healthy lives.

I am also eternally grateful for God entrusting me with the lives of my two sons. I am prayerful that I have been who He desires me to be and that I have poured into their lives what His desire for me was and continues to be. For these two amazing young men have been a blessing my life and in the lives of others. They are kind, loving, and intelligent men who understand the importance of their giftings and the ways they can pour life into others lives.

I would also like to share the importance for families to understand how "Generational Trauma" has and may continue to impact their life and their families lives (this was not a term that was known during the generations of my grandmother, mother, and my early years). For this is something that has impacted many generations of my family. This is why I feel it is so important for families to understand how important it is to address generational trauma(s) and to change the path for the next generations. I would encourage families to name and address the generational trauma(s), generational curses, and epigenetics in their families in order to change the trajectory of future generations. As this book speaks to Complex-PTSD, it is a book on the effects of trauma(s) and the importance of taking care of oneself and seeking professional help when it is needed.

TABLE OF CONTENTS

CHAPTER 1

UNDERSTANDING COMPLEX-POST TRAUMATIC STRESS DISORDER (CPTSD)

"You are exactly where you are meant to be in your life. You are not behind. You are not failing. You are not lost. You ARE learning. you ARE growing. You ARE healing. You ARE resilient".

"Most of the important things in the world have been accomplished by people who had kept on trying when there seemed to be no hope at all - Dale Carnegie.

Complex PTSD (which is sometimes interchanged with terms such as complex relational trauma, developmental trauma, and **in**terpersonal trauma) is a relatively recent concept. With the recognition of Complex-PTSD (C-PTSD) by the World Health Organization (WHO), healthcare providers around the world are gaining access to critical information about complex/chronic forms of trauma experienced by children and adults, including adult survivors of childhood abuse and neglect.

The World Health Organization (WHO) has included complex post-traumatic stress disorder (C-PTSD) in the final draft of the 11th edition of the International Classification of Diseases and Related Health Problems (ICD-11), which was published in June 2018 and was submitted to WHO's World Health Assembly for official endorsement in 2019. Mental health providers need to be informed about this diagnosis in order to provide effective treatment. Complex PTSD, or developmental PTSD as it is also called, refers to the constellation of symptoms that may result from prolonged, chronic exposure to traumatic experiences, especially in childhood, as opposed to PTSD which is more typically associated with a traumatic incident or set of traumatic events. According to the Clinical Psychology Review 2017 Dec; 58:1-15. It has been a controversial diagnosis and is not included in the fifth edition of the Diagnostic and Statistical Manual of Mental Disorders (DSM-5) which is used by Mental Health Professionals to make diagnosis.

The World Health Organization in its 2018 ICD-11 (International Classification of Diseases, (11th revision) introduced the new diagnosis of Complex Post traumatic Stress Disorder (C-PTSD). WHO introduced this diagnosis as a distinct but sibling condition to PTSD to reflect loss of emotional, psychological, and social resources in conditions of prolonged adversity.

The ICD-11 formulation of the two disorders follow from a long history of clinical observation that individuals who experienced chronic, repeated and prolonged traumas, such as childhood sexual abuse or domestic violence, tended to experience more complex reactions extending beyond those typically observed in PTSD and which included effects in three key domains: emotion regulation, self-identity and relational capacities.

PTSD has been recognized since approximately 1980, however Complex-PTSD is a fairly new term. Currently, the DSM-5 (Diagnostic and Statistical Manual of Mental Disorders) the Manual for Mental Health Assessments used by Clinicians, does not list C-

PTSD as a separate mental health diagnosis. However, the DSM-5 does include Post Traumatic Stress Disorder in a new category under Trauma and Stressor-Related Disorders.

Adult survivors of childhood abuse have historically often times been diagnosed with one or more mental health conditions that ignore the trauma history or trauma symptoms they are or have regularly experienced. C-PTSD is a disorder that may develop following exposure to a series of events of an extreme, prolonged, or repetitive nature that is experienced as extremely threatening or horrific and from which escape is difficult or impossible.

Many adult survivors of dysfunctional family systems and childhood abuse who enter into counseling often times also suffer from anxiety, panic attacks, depression and/or anger management issues. They may have been diagnosed in the past with Generalized Anxiety Disorder, Major Depressive Disorder, Acute Stress Disorder, Disinhibited Social Engagement disorder, Attention Deficit Hyperactive Disorder (ADHD, Bipolar Disorder, Obsessive-Compulsive Disorder (OCD), Borderline Personality Disorder an attachment disorder and even possibily Dissociative Identity Disorder (DID). They may also often present with codependency or addiction issues and may be in an unfulfilling or abusive relationship. Victims of Complex trauma may also experience dissociation. Dissociation is a state in which you feel emotionally detached from yourself.

The diagnosis is characterized by the core symptoms of PTSD, that is, all diagnostic requirements for PTSD have been met at some point during the course of the condition. In addition, C-PTSD is characterized by; severe and pervasive problems in affect regulation, persistent beliefs about oneself as diminished, defeated, or worthless, accompanied by deep and pervasive feelings of shame, guilt or failure related to the stressor; and persistent difficulties in sustaining relationships and in feeling close to others. This diagnosis tends to cause significant impairment in personal, family, social, educational, occupational, or other area of functioning.

After trauma, the world is experienced with a different nervous system. The survivor's energy now becomes focused on suppressing inner chaos, at the expense of spontaneous involvement in their lives. These attempts to maintain control over unbearable physiological experiences can result in a whole range of physical symptoms, including fibromyalgia, chronic fatigue, cancer, and other autoimmune diseases. This explains why it is critical for trauma treatment to engage the entire organism, body, mind, and brain according to Bessel van der Kolk, in his book The Body Keeps The Score.

At times you may feel stuck, however you do not have to stay there. You may be committed to certain patterns of behavior because they had helped you in the past. Now those behaviors may have become more harmful than helpful. The reason why you cannot move forward is because you keep applying an old formula to a new stage in your life. One must change the formula to get a different result (Emily Marontian). Traumas that were highly dangerous or abusive and threatened the life of those suffering will persist until addressed. The aftermath is lengthy, and the healing process may be a long road.

Individuals with a history of severe, continuous trauma over an extended period of time are at increased risk of C-PTSD. Onset of

C-PTSD is more likely if the victim is at a vulnerable stage of development (such as childhood) and dependent on the abuser for survival. Other risk factors include a family history of C-PTSD, and/or a chemical imbalance in the brain. While there are exceptional circumstances where adults develop C-PTSD, it is more often seen in those whose trauma occurred in childhood. However, it is not uncommon for it to happen in adulthood as well. For those who are older, being at the complete control of another (often unable to meet their most basic needs with them) coupled with no foreseeable end in sight, can break down a person's psyche, the survivor's sense of self, and affect them on a much deeper level. For those who go through this as children because the brain is still developing and they are just beginning to learn who they are as individuals, understand the world around them, and build their first relationships, severe trauma interrupts the entire course of the psychological and neurological development. C-PTSD is a serious mental health issue. However, symptoms can improve with treatment.

When you are resting because you are worn out, you need to remember that you are not wasting the day doing nothing. You are doing exactly what you need to do. You are recovering. Trauma survivors and thrivers may want to disappear, so they may dissociate or become quiet or isolate or do something else to hide themselves to become unseen. This may be because their voices have not been heard, are still not heard or worse, were heard and invalidated by being disregarded or disparaged or completely ridiculed. Sometimes one may think that they want to disappear, but all they really want is to be found.

Trauma victims often compete with others to see whose trauma is worse. The following metaphor says it all: "Someone who drowns in 7 feet of water is just as dead as someone who drowns in 20 feet of water". One must stop comparing their trauma to other people's trauma. **All trauma is excruciating**. It is not a competition.

Although one's abuse and trauma may be different, everyone will suffer, and it is the suffering that makes you the same; it is what bonds you together. In your similarity and in your bond, everyone can help one another heal because they know and understand the flashbacks, the symptoms, the lack of understanding from family and friends, and so many other things. So, do not worry about the level of your abuse. Just tell your story because it is your truth, let it heal you! It may also help someone else to heal.

Not all survivors have invisible triggers. Sometimes it can be a smell, a song, or seeing someone in the street who looks just like your abuser. In an instance, one may feel like the ground is shaking. One may lose their footing. Yet nobody around you can tell the difference.

There can be a constant struggle between your heart and your mind. Your heart may hope that things will get better, but your mind may not know if it will.

Victims of CPTSD may also experience dissociation. Dissociation is a state in which you feel emotionally detached from yourself. Survivors of complex trauma often report their abuse as if they watched it happen to another person or have lost memory of some or much of the trauma. Children who have been abused by the people they are supposed to trust are at high risk of dissociation.

Based on extensive research, C-PTSD is a more severe diagnosis than PTSD. The new diagnosis includes the symptoms of PTSD and *adds* a second component of Disturbances of Self-Organization (DSO) — affective dysregulation and struggles with identity. C-PTSD comprises six symptom clusters:

A first order of three PTSD symptom clusters:

1. Re-experiencing of the trauma in the here and now

2. Avoidance of traumatic reminders

3. A persistent sense of current threat that is manifested by exaggerated startle and hypervigilance

A second order of three additional symptom clusters that reflect disturbances of self-organization resulting from prolonged exposure to adversity:

4. Affective dysregulation

5. Negative self-concept

6. Disturbances in relationships

The additional three symptom clusters reflect a loss of emotional, psychological, and social resources resulting from frequent trauma, a greater accumulation of different types of childhood traumatic experiences, and higher levels of functional impairment. Symptom endorsement rates for PTSD and DSO were equally high, suggesting that the two components of the disorder are equally important.

Preliminary finding from WHO suggest that CPTSD is common in clinical and general population samples, although there may be variations in prevalence across countries. WHO also found the following initial findings:

- CPTSD is a more common condition than PTSD.
- Multiple cumulative childhood interpersonal violence was a stronger predictor of CPTSD than of PTSD in both clinical and population samples.
- CPTSD is a more debilitating condition compared to PTSD with regard to survivor functioning. CPTSD was associated with greater comorbid symptoms and substantially lower psychological well-being, suggesting a greater severity than PTSD.
- Women compared to men were more than twice as likely to meet criteria for PTSD AND CPTSD.
- The most frequently endorsed symptom cluster was negative self-concept, suggesting the critical role problems in self-concept may play in CPTSD.

As has been stated previously, Complex Post-Traumatic Stress Disorder (CPTSD) is a complicated diagnosis that has yet to appear in the *Diagnostic and Statistical Manual of Mental Disorders* (DSM-5). CPTSD usually involves traumatic and long-term abuse. The following are a few examples of its causes. Basically, CPTSD forms when a person feels they are in a situation from where they cannot escape. To survive the emotional and physical trauma perpetrated on them by their abusers, these individuals learn to push emotions deep down inside to make them virtually irretrievable.

The following are a few examples of its cause (this list is by no means exhaustive):

- Sexual abuse
- Emotional abuse
- Neglect
- Physical Abuse
- Mental Abuse
- Domestic Violence
- Human Trafficking
- Living as a Prison of War
- Living in a War Zone
- Surviving in a Concentration or Internment Camp
- First Responders who experience virtually daily exposure to traumatic events
- Car Accident
- Natural Disasters
- Mugging
- Rape
- War
- Abandonment
- Neglect

Trauma can affect a person's emotional, physical, and psychological well-being in various ways. Everyone's trauma is unique, and one's response to a traumatic event is also unique. The American Psychiatric Association (2013) identified the following responses a person may experience:

- flashbacks
- trouble sleeping
- avoidance of people or places that may trigger an emotional reaction
- dread
- an overall feeling of numbness
- difficulty sleeping/nightmares
- anxiety
- self-destructive behavior
- difficulty concentrating
- aggression or
- difficulty with memory and cognition

In the healing process, self-care is extremely important and involves exercising and getting good nutrition, obtaining adequate sleep, having positive/healthy support systems at a mininal. Sometimes it's spending time with loved ones or taking a nap. And sometimes it is binge watching an entire season on TV in one weekend while you lounge around in your pajamas. Whatever soothes you soul is a good thing. We will talk more extensively about the importance of self-care and self-love and what it looks like.

Complex-PTSD Versus PTSD

Complex PTSD differs from PTSD in that the trauma sufferer has been exposed to repeated and prolonged traumatic events which, in many cases, may apply to a dysfunctional, abusive, or otherwise traumatizing family environment or other traumatic event(s).

There are several differences between CPTSD and simple PTSD. CPTSD is linked with severe, ongoing trauma or multiple types of trauma where the victim has no hope of escape. PTSD may be triggered by a brief one-time event such as a car crash, armed attack, or natural disaster. CPTSD has severe symptoms that impair everyday functioning. Symptoms of PTRSD may range from mile to severe. People with CPTSD may experience all the symptoms typically associated with PTSD plus additional symptoms.

While there is a fundamental difference in the two diagnoses of CPTSD and PTSD, there are some striking similarities when it comes to treating them.

As noted earlier, Complex Post-Traumatic Stress Disorder (CPTSD) is a complicated and a new diagnosis that has yet to appear in the Diagnostic and Statistical Manual of Mental Disorders (DSM-5). One of the primary differences between PTSD and CPTSD is that post-traumatic stress disorder results from a single event, where complex post-traumatic stress disorder forms in relation to a series of traumatic events. Healing may take decades or an entire lifetime.

These events, while highly traumatizing, can be resolved with emotional support from either friends/family, psychotherapy, and/or medication. However, CPTSD usually involves traumatic and long-term abuse: physical, emotional, or sexual in scope.

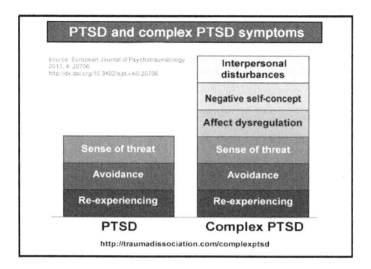

Symptoms of Complex-PTSD

Interpersonal problems include social and interpersonal avoidance (avoiding relationships) or cut off from others, and never feeling close to another person.

Negative self-concept involves feelings of worthlessness and guilt. While survivors of PTSD may feel not themselves, a survivor of Complex PTSD may feel no sense of self at all or experience a changed personality.

Interpersonal sensitivity includes having feelings which are easily hurt, anger/temper outbursts and difficulties with interpersonal relationships. Complex PTSD is normally the result of interpersonal trauma, the long duration of the trauma and the control of the perpetrator(s) prevents people from expressing anger or range at the perpetrator(s) during the trauma; anger and rage both at perpetrators and the self can only be fully expressed after the trauma ends. Prolonged abuse normally leads to a loss of previously held beliefs, with feelings of being forsaken by both man and God.

Affect dysregulation means being unable to manage your own emotions and is often referred to as difficulties with emotional regulation. The unexpressed anger and internalized range resulting from the trauma may lead to self-destructive or reckless/risk taking behaviors, e.g., self-harm and/or suicide attempts, which may be driven by a sense of self-hatred.

People with Complex PTSD also meet the diagnostic criteria for PTSD, which are a persistent sense of threat, e.g., hypervigilance and being easily startled, avoiding reminders of the traumas, and re-experiencing or reliving the traumas, for example flashbacks and intrusive thoughts about the trauma.

Feelings of shame or guilt; difficulty controlling your emotions; periods of losing attention and concentration (dissociation); physical symptom (headaches, dizziness, chest pains, stomach aches) • Cutting yourself off from friends and family; relationship difficulties; destructive or risky behavior, such as self-harm, alcohol abuse, or drug abuse; suicidal thoughts. Trauma can be buried for so long a time even when we think we have deal with it. A catalyst usually unearths the trauma and then we have no option but to experience and process it.

There are many severe emotional, mental, and relational issues associated with complex post-traumatic disorder. These issues may cause significant impairment in day-to-day functioning. Individual with CPTSD may experience: Hyperarousal, avoidance of people, place, or things that are reminders of the trauma, low mood, dissociation, uncontrolled anger, self-destructive behavior, night-mare of the trauma, flashbacks of the trauma, an ongoing search for a rescuer, preoccupation with revenge, relationship issues, trust issues, hopelessness, worthlessness, or despair, intense guilt or shame, social isolation, digestive issues, sexual promiscuity, physical or medical issues, amnesia/DID, Suicidal ideation(s).

Interpersonal problems includes social and interpersonal avoidance (avoiding relationships), feeling distance or cut off from others, and never feeling close to another person.

Negative self-concept involves feelings of worthlessness and guilt. While survivors of PTSD may feel "not myself", a survivor of Complex PTSD may feel no sense of self at all or experience a changed personality; a few may feel as if they are no longer human at all (Lovelace and McGrady, 1980; Timerman, 1981).

Interpersonal sensitivity includes having feelings which are easily hurt, anger/temper outbursts and difficulties with interpersonal relationships. Complex PTSD is normally the result of interpersonal trauma, the long duration of the trauma and the control of the perpetrator(s) prevents people from expressing anger or rage at the perpetrator(s) during the trauma; anger and rage both at perpetrators and the self can only be fully expressed after the trauma ends. Prolonged abuse normally leads to a loss of previously held beliefs, with feelings of "being forsaken by both man and God".

Affect dysregulation means being unable to manage your own emotions and is often referred to as "difficulties with emotional regulation". The unexpressed anger and internalized rage resulting from the trauma may lead to self-destructive or reckless/risk taking behaviors, e.g., self-harm and/or suicide attempts, which may be driven by a sense of self-hatred.

People with Complex PTSD also meet the diagnostic criteria for PTSD which are:

- a persistent sense of threat, e.g., hypervigilance and being easily startled
- avoiding reminders of the traumas,
- and re-experiencing or reliving the traumas, for example flashbacks and intrusive thoughts about the trauma.

In addition to the symptoms above, survivors of prolonged child abuse have an increased risk of both self-injury and **repeated victimization**, for example relationships with abusive people, sexual harassment, and rape.

The survivor's difficulties are all too easily attributed to underlying character problems, even when the trauma is known. When the trauma is kept secret, as is frequently the case in sexual and domestic violence, the survivor's symptoms and behavior may appear quite baffling, not only to lay people but also sometimes to mental health professionals.

Gateway to C-PTSD

- Cannabis/drugs is not the gateway.
- Alcohol is not the gateway.
- Nicotine is not the gateway.
- Caffeine is not the gateway.
- Trauma is the gateway.
- Abuse is the gateway.

- Molestation is the gateway.
- Neglect is the gateway.

Drug abuse, violent behavior, hypersexuality and self-harm are often symptoms (not the cause) of much bigger issues. And it almost always stems from a childhood filled with trauma, absent parents, and/or an abusive family. Although it can also stem from traumatic experiences in adulthood that are consistent and ongoing. One of the key's to understanding is to: **Communicate, Empathize, and Rehabilitate**.

Adverse Childhood Experiences (ACE) Pyramid

The Adverse Childhood Experiences (ACE) Study is one of the largest investigations ever conducted to assess associations between childhood exposure to traumatic stressors and later-life health and well-being. The study is a collaboration between the Centers for Disease Control and Prevention and Kaiser Permanente's Health Appraisal Clinic in San Diego. The ACE Study findings suggest that certain experiences are major risk factors for the leading causes of illness and death as well as poor quality of life in the United States. Progress in preventing and recovering from the nation's worst health and social problems is likely to benefit from understanding that many of these problems arise as a consequence of adverse childhood experiences. The ACE Pyramid represents the conceptual framework for the study and was designed to assess what was considered to be scientific gaps about the origins of risk factors. These gaps are depicted as the two arrows linking Adverse Childhood Experiences to risk factors that lead to the health and social consequences higher up the pyramid. Specifically, the study was designed to provide data that would help answer the question: "If risk factors for disease, disability, and early mortality are not randomly distributed, what influences precede the adoption or development of them?" By providing information to answer this question, they hoped to provide scientific information that would be useful for developing new and more effective prevention programs. The ACE Study takes a whole-life perspective from birth to death. By working within this framework, the ACE Study began to progressively uncover how adverse childhood experiences (ACE) are strongly related to development and prevalence of risk factors for disease and health and social well-being throughout the lifespan (See pyramid).

There are 10 types of childhood traumas measured in the ACE study. Five are personal-physical abuse, verbal abuse, sexual abuse, physical neglect and emotional neglect. Five are related to other family members—a parent who's an alcoholic, a mother who's a victim of domestic violence, a family member in jail, a family member diagnosed with a mental illness, and the disappearance of a parent through divorce, death, or abandonment. Each type of trauma counts as one. There are, of course, many other types of childhood trauma—watching a sibling being abused, losing a caregiver (grandmother, mother, grandfather, etc.), homelessness, surviving and recovering from a severe accident, witnessing a father being abused by a mother, witnessing a grandmother abusing a father, and so on. The ACE Study included only those 10 childhood traumas because those were mentioned as most common by a group of about 300 Kaiser members; those traumas were also well studied individually in the research literature. The most important thing to remember is that the ACE score is meant as a **guideline**: If you experienced other types of toxic stress over months or years, then those would likely increase your risk of health consequences as well as PTSD and Complex-PTSD. As your ACE score increases, so does the risk of disease, social and emotional problems. With an ACE score of 4 or more, things are starting to get serious.

The study revealed that traumatizing childhood events are commonplace. Two-thirds of individuals reported at least one traumatizing childhood event. Forty percent of the patients reported two or more traumatizing childhood events, and 12.5 percent reported four or more. These results were then correlated with the physical health of the interviewed patients and researchers discovered a dose-response. Traumatizing events in childhood were linked to adult disease in all categories—cancer, heart disease, chronic pain, autoimmune diseases, bone fractures, high blood pressure, obesity, diabetes, depression, smoking, and suicide. The average age of patients in this study was 57 years old, which means that childhood trauma can have a delayed effect on the body, making it entirely possible that something that happened 50 years ago may be predisposing someone to illness in the here and now.

The more Adverse Childhood Events an individual reported, the more resistant to treatment they were. A highly recommended book on this topic is The Body Keeps the Score Brain, Mind and Body in the Healing of Trauma by Bessel van der Kolk.

Subsequent to the ACE Study, other ACE surveys have expanded the types of ACEs to include racism, gender discrimination, witnessing a sibling being abused, witnessing violence outside the home, witnessing a father being abused by a mother, being bullied by a peer or adult, involvement with the foster care system, living in a war zone, living in an unsafe neighborhood, losing a family member to deportation, etc.

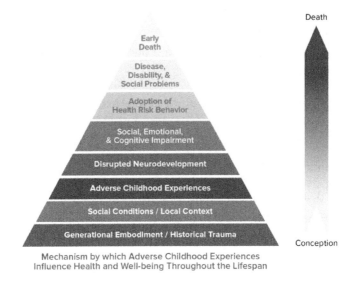

Mechanism by which Adverse Childhood Experiences
Influence Health and Well-being Throughout the Lifespan

Several studies have demonstrated that patients exposed to trauma-induced stress in their first eight years of life are more likely to develop mood disorders, psychotic disorders, and PTSD and/or Complex-PTSD than children who are not exposed to trauma.

Treatment for Complex-PTSD

Complex PTSD is harder to treat/recover from than 'simple' PTSD; not only are there multiple traumas but the interpersonal and long-term nature of the traumas lead to additional symptoms. Repeated child abuse is the most common cause of Complex PSTD. The International Society of Traumatic Stress Studies publishes Complex Posttraumatic Stress Disorder treatment guidelines which are based on psychotherapy using a three-phase approach.

Phase 1 focuses on improving the individual's safety, reducing symptoms and skills training, which increases the person's emotional, social, and psychological competencies. This often involves medication. Improving safety refers to reducing unsafe behaviors, e.g., self-harm, and risk taking, and if possible, establishing a safe environment.

Phase 2 focuses on processing of the unresolved trauma memories. This results in memories being integrated into an "adaptive representation of self, relationships and the world" and should be done using individual rather than group therapy.

Phase 3 involves consolidating treatment gains, including using these gains to engage more in interpersonal relationships, work/education, and the community/life in general.

CPTSD is usually treated with psychotherapy, medication, or a combination of both approaches and self-care. Types of psychotherapy that have been proven to be effective include the following:

- Cognitive behavioral therapy (CBT)
- Prolonged exposure therapy (PE)
- Cognitive restructuring therapy
- Dialectical behavior therapy (DBT)
- Eye Movement Desensitization and Reprocessing (EMDR)

Cognitive Behavioral Therapy (CBT)

Cognitive behavioral therapy is a form of psychological treatment that has been demonstrated to be effective for a range of problems including depression, anxiety, substance use, marital problems, eating disorders and PTSD/CPTSD. Numerous research studies suggest that CBS leads to significant improvement in functioning and quality of life. CBT has been demonstrated to be as effective as other forms of psychological therapy/psychiatric medications. CBT is based on several core principles, including: (1.) Psychological problems are based, in part , on faulty or unhelpful ways of thinking. (2).) Psychological problems are based, in part, on learned patterns of unhelpful behavior. (3.) People suffering from psychological problems can learn better ways of coping with them, thereby relieving their symptoms and experiencing healthier lifestyles. CBT treatment usually involves efforts to change thinking patterns. These strategies may include: Learning to recognize one's distortions in thinking that are creating problems, and then to reevaluate them in light of reality. Gaining a better understanding of the behavior and motivation of others. Using problem solving skills to cope with difficult situations. Learning to develop a greater sense of confidence in one's ow abilities. CBT treatment also usually involves efforts to change behavioral patterns. The changes include facing one's fears instead of avoiding them, using role playing to prepare for potentially problematic interactions with others and learning to calm one's mind and relax one's body.

Prolonged Exposure Therapy (PE)

Prolonged exposure therapy (**PE**) is a form of behavioral therapy and cognitive behavioral therapy designed to treat post-traumatic stress disorder. It is characterized by two main treatment procedures (imaginal and in vivo exposures). Imaginal exposure is repeated "on purpose" retelling of the trauma memory. In vivo exposure is gradually confronting situations, places and things that are reminders of the trauma or feelings of danger (despite being safe). Prolonged exposure therapy was developed by Edna B Foa, Director of the Center for the Treatment and Study of Anxiety at the University of Pennsylvania. Prolonged Exposure therapy is theoretically based and highly effective treatment for chronic PTSD and related depression, anxiety, and anger. PE falls under the category of "exposure-based therapy" and is supported by scientific studies which reflect its positive impact on patient symptoms.

Many people who have experienced a trauma try to avoid thoughts and feelings associated with the event. Similarly, many individuals also avoid situations, places and activities that remind them of the trauma or that just feel scary. However, while avoiding can make one feel more comfortable in the short term, it actually can me the problem work in the long term because it prevents one from overcoming their fears. Imaginal and in vivo exposures address these problems and work in similar ways.

Exposure based therapy focuses on confronting the harmless cues/triggers of trauma/stress in order to unpair them from the feelings of anxiety and stress associated. Prolonged exposure is a flexible therapy that can be modified to fit the needs of the individual client.

It is specifically designed to help clients psychologically process traumatic events and reduce trauma induced psychological disturbances

Cognitive restructuring Therapy (CR)

Cognitive restructuring (CR) is a psychotherapeutic process of learning to identify and dispute irrational or maladaptive thoughts known as cognitive distortions, such as all-or-nothing thinking (splitting), magical thinking, over-generalization, magnification, and emotional reasoning, which are commonly associated with many mental health disorders. CR employs many strategies, such as Socratic questioning, thought recording, and guided imagery, and is used in many types of therapies, including cognitive behavioral therapy (CBT) and rational emotive behavior therapy (REBT). A number of studies demonstrate considerable efficacy in using CR-based therapies. Cognitive therapy operated un the principle that thoughts, belief systems, and biases influence both the emotions an individual experiences and the intensity of those emotions.

The goals of Cognitive restructuring therapy is:

1. to have a greater understanding of what PTSD is and how it has impacted your life.

2. to feel a greater sense of control over symptoms of PTSD.

3. to experience a reduction in symptoms of PTSD.

Cognitive restructuring has four steps:

1. identify the negative thoughts/fears

2. consider if the fears are rational or not

3. develop positive coping statements/strategies

4. incorporate positive coping statements into one's life

Dialectical Behavior Therapy (DBT)

Dialectical Behavioral Therapy has proven to be effective for those who struggle with PTSD and emotional dysregulation. DBT focuses on improving emotional-management problems and the problem behaviors that they cause. Therapies that are often included in this therapy included: mindfulness meditation skills, interpersonal effectiveness skills, distress tolerance skills, emotional regulation skills. DBT focuses on changing a person's thoughts and beliefs about themselves which motivated the changing of behavior. The main focus of DBT is to help individuals learn skills that will decrease emotional dysregulation, self-destructive behaviors, and other unhealthy coping mechanisms.

Dialectical behavior therapy (DBT) is a type of cognitive-behavioral therapy. Its main goals are to teach people how to live in the moment, develop healthy ways to cope with stress, regulate their emotions, and improve their relationships with others. Some of the strategies and techniques that are used in DBT include:

Core Mindfulness

One important benefit of DBT is the development of mindfulness skills. Mindfulness helps you focus on the present or "live in the moment." This helps you pay attention to what is happening inside you (your thoughts, feelings, sensations, and impulses) as well as using your senses to tune in to what's happening around you (what you see, hear, smell, and touch) in nonjudgmental ways.

Mindfulness skills help you slow down and focus on using healthy coping skills when you are in the midst of emotional pain. This strategy can also help you stay calm and avoid engaging in automatic negative thought patterns and impulsive behavior.

Distress Tolerance

Distress tolerance skills help you accept yourself and your current situation. You will four techniques for handling a crisis:

- Distraction
- Improving the moment
- Self-soothing
- Thinking of the pros and cons of not tolerating distress

Distress tolerance techniques help prepare you for intense emotions and empower you to cope with them with a more positive long-term outlook.

Interpersonal Effectiveness

Interpersonal effectiveness helps you to become more assertive in a relationship (for example, expressing your needs and be able to say "no") while still keeping a relationship positive and healthy. You will learn to listen and communicate more effectively, deal with challenging people, and respect yourself and others.

Emotion Regulation

Emotion regulation lets you navigate powerful feelings in a more effective way. The skills you learn will help you to identify, name, and change your emotions. When you are able to recognize and cope with intense negative emotions (for example, anger), it reduces your emotional vulnerability and helps you have more positive emotional experiences.

Emotion-management problems stem from a combination of:

- Biology (such as a person's tendency to experience emotions intensely).
- A childhood environment where emotions were ignored or where expressing them was punished.

Eye Movement Desensitization and Reprocessing (EMDR).

Eye movement desensitization and reprocessing is a form of psychotherapy developed by Francine Sharpiro starting 1988 in which the individual being treated is asked to recall distressing images, which will be addressed through bilateral stimulation, such as side-to-side eye movements or hand tapping. According to the 2013 World Health Organization practice guidelines: "This therapy is based on the idea that negative thoughts, feelings and behaviors are the result of unprocessed memories. The treatment involved standardized procedures that include focusing simultaneously on spontaneous associations of traumatic images, thoughts emotions and bodily sensations and bilateral stimulation that is most commonly in the form of repeated eye movements."

EYE MOVEMENT DESENSITIZATION AND REPROCESSING

- Created by Francine Shapiro in 1987.

- Bilateral stimulation through eye movements
- Natural way brain processes information and heals self(REM Sleep)

- Treats PTSD and a wide range of mental health issues.

- Trauma overloads the brains natural coping mechanism.

- Unprocessed memories and feelings are stored in limbic system of your brain in a "raw" and emotional form, rather than in a verbal "story" mode. These memories can be continually triggered when a person experiences event similar to past traumatic events.

- EMDR helps create connections between memories, enabling the brain to process the traumatic memory in a very natural way.

Phase 1: The first phase is a history-taking session(s). The therapist assesses the client's readiness and develops a treatment plan. Client and therapist identify possible targets for EMDR processing. These include distressing memories and current situations that cause emotional distress. Other targets may include related incidents in the past. Emphasis is placed on the development of specific skills and behaviors that will be needed by the client in future situations.

Initial EMDR processing may be directed to childhood events rather than to adult-onset stressors or the identified critical incident if the client had a problematic childhood. Clients generally gain insight on their situations; the emotional distress resolves and they start to change their behaviors. The length of treatment depends upon the number of traumas and the age of PTSD onset. Generally, those with single event adult-onset trauma can be successfully treated in under 5 hours. Multiple trauma victims may require a longer treatment time.

Phase 2: During the second phase of treatment, the therapist ensures that the client has several different ways of handling emotional distress. The therapist may teach the client a variety of imagery and stress reduction techniques the client can use during and between sessions. A goal of EMDR therapy is to produce rapid and effective change while the client maintains equilibrium during and between sessions.

Phases 3-6: In phases three to six, a target is identified and processed using EMDR therapy procedures. These involve the client identifying three things:

1. The vivid visual image related to the memory

2. A negative belief about oneself

3. Related emotions and body sensations.

In addition, the client identifies a positive belief. The therapist helps the client rate the positive belief as well as the intensity of the negative emotions. After this, the client is instructed to focus on the image, negative thought, and body sensations while simultaneously engaging in EMDR processing using sets of bilateral stimulation. These sets may include eye movements, taps, or tones. The type and length of these sets is different for each client. At this point, the EMDR client is instructed to just notice whatever spontaneously happens.

After each set of stimulation, the clinician instructs the client to let his/her mind go blank and to notice whatever thought, feeling, image, memory, or sensation comes to mind. Depending upon the client's report, the clinician will choose the next focus of attention. These repeated sets with directed focused attention occur numerous times throughout the session. If the client becomes distressed or has difficulty in progressing, the therapist follows established procedures to help the client get back on track.

When the client reports no distress related to the targeted memory, (s)he is asked to think of the preferred positive belief that was identified at the beginning of the session. At this time, the client may adjust the positive belief if necessary, and then focus on it during the next set of distressing events.

Phase 7: In phase seven, closure, the therapist asks the client to keep a log during the week. The log should document any related material that may arise. It serves to remind the client of the self-calming activities that were mastered in phase two.

Phase 8: The next session begins with phase eight. Phase eight consists of examining the progress made thus far. The EMDR treatment processes all related historical events, current incidents that elicit distress, and future events that will require different responses.

Although it can be difficult to cope with the symptoms of CPTSD, there are several steps you can take to manage the condition. It is recommended that one:

- Learn as much as you can about CPTSD
- Seek professional care
- Stay in touch with your loved ones
- Monitor your symptoms and learn about your triggers

- Learn and use relaxation techniques
- Join a support group
- Take part in activities you enjoy
- Write about how you feel
- Exercise regularly
- Avoid alcohol and unprescribed drugs
- Engage in spiritual activities
- Find healthy ways to distract yourself from negative thoughts

Through neuro-imaging studies, Dr. Daniel Amen has documented people experiencing calming in their limbic structures following Eye Movement Desensitization and Reprocessing (EMDR) treatment. Other venues for limbic calming include soothing music, prayer, meditation, mindful breathing, yoga, and exercise. The following activities can encourage limbic calming:

- Take 5 minutes in the morning and evening to rock back and forth, or side to side, paying attention and relaxing the body.
- Find music or tones of music, with our without words, that bring you into a state of calmness.
- Practice deep breathing in sequences of three. For example, breathe, breathe, breathe. Rest. Breathe, breathe, breathe. Rest...
- Practice some form of exercise for 12-15 minutes per day to increase serotonin and dopamine.
- Pray or meditate for 5-10 minutes per day, as the spiritual center of the brain is able to influence and calm the deeper regions of the brain.

CHAPTER 2

"What you're looking for is not out there, it is in you."

The "window of tolerance" was originally coined by Dr. Dan Siegel to describe the optimal zone of arousal in which a person would be able to function and deal with day-to-day stress most effectively (*The Developing Mind*, 2020).

Most people can deal with the demands and stress of everyday life without much difficulty, however, for those who have experienced trauma, anxiety, or other mental illness, it can be difficult to stay in your optimal zone. Recognizing your window of tolerance and what happens to you physically and emotionally is an important first step. This knowledge enables you to widen your window of tolerance and improve that optimal zone.

Deviating from your window of tolerance is still likely to occur during your road to recovery. When one becomes dysregulated, there are many self-regulating techniques one can utilize to bring yourself back.

The window of tolerance is the zone where intense emotional arousal can be processed in a healthy way, allowing one to function and react to stress or anxiety effectively. It allows you to respond to the demands and stress of everyday life without much difficulty. It is the comfort zone in which we have the ability to self-soothe and self-regulate our emotional state.

Try and think of a time when you were in a balanced calm state of mind, when you felt relaxed and in control. Do you remember feeling calm, grounded, alert, safe, and present? This is what it feels like when you are in the optimal zone.

How Trauma Can Affect Your Window of Tolerance

When the balance is interfered with, either due to trauma or extreme stress, one ends up leaving their window of tolerance. One's body typically reacts defensively to this change in emotional state. This is when you will begin to dysregulate, and experience fight or flight responses. If it is not possible to fight or flee, your body will collapse into the freeze state.

When the body responds defensively, it is just trying to keep you safe. This is a normal response when you are put in an unsafe situation(s). However, trauma and extreme stress can create these similar responses that sticks with one, even long after the event has passed.

Any undue stress or anxiety generates fear and negativity that could result in your body triggering these defenses. This is because your mind thinks the trauma or extreme stress you experienced in the past is reoccurring.

Dysregulation occurs when you start to deviate outside your window of tolerance, and you will start to feel agitated or anxious. You do not feel comfortable, but you are not out of control yet. Past this point is when one's body's defenses start to take over. One may experience various symptoms such as anxiety, and you may begin to feel out of control. This is when fight, flight or freeze responses occur. These two states known as hyperarousal and hypo arousal occur when one dysregulates. In these three states you may experience a variety of symptoms.

Hyperarousal is characterized by excessive activation or energy. You will usually experience a heightened sense of anxiety, which may make you more sensitive or overly responsive to things that occur in your daily life. The fight and flight responses occur in the hyperarousal state, and you may experience symptoms such as anxiety, panic, fear, hypervigilance, defensiveness, and anger. Hyperarousal also keeps your mind "stuck" and makes it difficult to sleep, eat, manage emotions, or concentrate. If hyperarousal reaches the most intensified level, this may result in dissociative rage and hostility.

Hypo-arousal is the complete opposite of hyperarousal. This experience of too little arousal is the result of a freeze response, which can cause such symptoms as numbness, absence of feelings, lack of energy, inability to think or respond, reduced physical movement, and/or being ashamed. Hypo arousal can also impact your sleep and eating habits, leaving you feeling emotionally flat. You may be unable to express yourself, process thoughts and emotions, or respond physically. Throughout your day you deal with the demands and stresses life throws at you. This is known as smooth sailing because you can sail throughout the day positively dealing with any challenges. Dysregulation occurs when you are deviating from the smooth sailing path. You begin to feel uncomfortable, agitated, or anxious, but you are still in control. Ideally, you want to bring yourself back into the window of tolerance at this point. This is because you are still in control and it offers the least amount of resistance. To bring yourself back use self-regulating techniques (which I will discuss later in this book). If you cannot bring yourself back into this optimal state you will deviate to the hyperarousal or hypo arousal states and experience fight, flight, or freeze responses or fawn response.

Fawn Response –Peter Walker describes, the "fawn response" is one of four defensive reactions to ongoing trauma. Those who fawn tend to put the needs and wants of others ahead of their own at the cost of the health of their own egos, and the protection of and compassion for themselves. A fawn response is brought about by the attempt to avoid conflict and trauma by appeasing people. For children, this can be defined as a need to be a "good kid" in order to escape mistreatment by an abusive or neglectful parent. As an adult, this, can mean that in relationships you are consistently ignoring your own needs, values, and boundaries to conform to what you believe others expect of you.

It may be difficult at first to determine if fawning is one's innate response to protecting yourself from trauma. Here are a few *key signs of fawning*:

You Have an Inability to Say "No"

You're pushed to the brink with work and social commitments, and you are feeling both physically and emotionally drained. Yet when someone asks you for a favor, you just cannot manage to say "no." Internally you're likely dreading all you have signed up for, but that feeling somehow isn't enough to start declining requests.

Your Values seem to be Fluid in Personal Interactions

What can start off as feeling like you are just trying to avoid a fight can become a running theme throughout nearly all of your inter- actions. You find you have a very hard time standing up for yourself and what you believe is right, particularly with people that you are close to. It can be little things, like your personal preference on a movie, as well as more serious issues, like validating a behavior or viewpoint that you actually disagree with.

Your Guilt and Anger Go Hand-in-Hand

You are so used to putting the feelings of others before your own that somehow feeling angry at someone feels like a betrayal. You end up suppressing these feelings or overly sympathizing with the other person, even when they are clearly in the wrong.

You are Blanking out Emotionally

While you go about trying to make everyone around you happy, you begin to unconsciously repress your own emotions to the point of being disconnected from them. If you are trying to name how you feel, but are getting caught up in a complex tangle of guilt, anger, fear, and anxiety, it's likely that you have disassociated from your primary emotional responses.

Your Emotions Erupt in Unusual Ways

Regular suppression of emotions can cause them to emerge in un- related situations, such as when you're talking to a stranger, or in the midst of a seemingly normal activity. You may feel an uncon- trollable urge to vent or cry, and wonder where it is coming from.

You Feel Responsible for the Reactions of Others

Because you are so invested in the validation and happiness of others, you even feel responsible for how they react. For example, when a friend doesn't like a movie, you have suggested, you may feel bad and apologetic. Or, in your relationships, you are constantly explaining someone's bad behavior as somehow your fault. This is also related to codependency, and is often accompanied by anxiety, guilt, and self-loathing.

You Feel like No One Really Knows You

Based on the fact that you are likely repressing many of the emotions that make you fully "you," you may end up feeling like even those you are close to don't really know who you are.

For those struggling with the effects of the fawning response, therapy is an important source of support and growth. Many find that even when they are aware of fawning behavior and the negative impacts resulting from it, they still feel it is challenging to break out of it as their default response. This is due to the deeply ingrained idea that fawning will create safety.

Therapists suggest that to successfully begin to positively alter this innate response, the root causes of trauma must be directly addressed. This allows you time to process, grieve, and rebuild a life that is not dictated by fear.

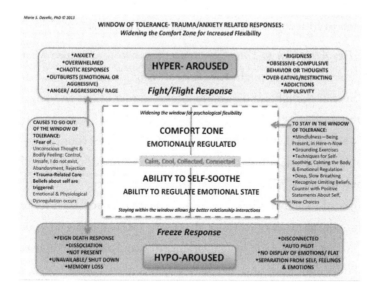

How to Recognize Your Window of Tolerance

Understanding how something makes you feel emotionally and physically gives you an understanding of where you are in your window of tolerance. If you can recognize your symptoms, you will be better prepared to be able to bring yourself back into that comfortable space. Recognizing your own window of tolerance will help you self-regulate. The lack of awareness makes it difficult to self-regulate because one may not even be aware of what is happening. Recognizing your own window of tolerance will help you self-regulate. The lack of awareness makes it difficult to self-regulate because one may not even be aware of what is happening.

Four steps in recognizing your Window of Tolerance

1.   *Pay Attention to Your Symptoms.* When you recognize what you are experiencing might not be right, pause for a moment. Focus on your thoughts and pay attention to the emotions and physical responses of your body. Think about what you are feeling, what you were doing that would have caused this, and how your body is reacting. Understanding the way an individual functions is critical to maintaining a balance. Being aware of when you are within your window of tolerance allows you to leverage that to accomplish the things you needs. Try to think about what is happening to your body when you are experiencing undue stress and anxiety. You may not know right away and may have to pay more attention to your body and feelings the next time. Try to identify a few at first. If the symptom you experienced is not listed, there are a few areas for you to write down your own symptom on the bottom of the worksheet. I encourage you to do so, as everyone's experience is unique. These symptoms include feelings, thoughts, and physical responses. This awareness is the first important step in learning to manage and control the stress or anxiety you experience. Without first being aware of what is happening to you, you cannot manage it well.

2.   *Identify Symptoms You Experience.* The next step is to identify what symptoms you experience due to stress or anxiety cause by daily life.

These symptoms are generally categorized into hyperarousal and hypo-arousal. Again, write down the symptoms you experienced as noted above. I encourage you to do so as everyone's experience is unique to them, this includes the feelings, thoughts, and physical responses.

3. ***Identify Distress Level.*** Next, you want to identify the level of distress the symptoms make you feel. For each symptom, rank from 1 to 5, with 1 the least severe and 5 the most extreme and paralyzing. Consider your emotions and any physical distress you may experience. By ranking the severity, it helps you to understand which symptoms will occur when you are just starting to experience dysregulation, and which are so severe you are no longer in control of your body.

4. ***Identify the Cause.*** Think back to when you may have been experiencing the hyperarousal and hypo arousal symptoms. Try to identify the cause or trigger of the dysregulation by focusing on what you may have been doing at that time. Was it something someone said to you? or Were you thinking about something in particular? By identifying the cause or trigger you can better be prepared the next time if/when it occurs. If it is something in your control, avoiding the same situation would be ideal, but it isn't always practical. The next steps will teach you how to bring yourself back into the window of tolerance when/if it does happen.

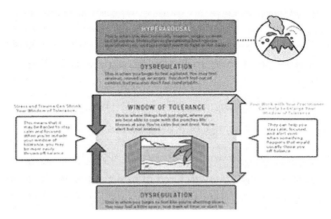

How to Manage your Window of Tolerance

Learning to manage your window of tolerance will enable you to deal with the demands of life. There are two ways to stay within your optimal zone: Widen your Window of Tolerance and work on Self-Regulating. Widening your window of tolerance helps to keep you in the optimal zone longer, so you are less likely to dysregulate when you experience the stress of anxiety. Self-regulating helps you process stress and anxiety and helps to bring you back into the window of tolerance so you can deal with the demands of life. Think of your window of tolerance as a river and you are floating down the middle of that river. When you expand your window of tolerance, the river widens, and the flow slows down. You are comfortable and safe floating down the calm waters. However, when you experience adversity, trauma, undue stress, or anxiety, your window of tolerance shrinks, and the river begins to narrow and speed up. You start to feel uncomfortable, unsafe and have difficulty keeping yourself afloat. There are five ways we can increase one's window of tolerance and maintain that safe comfortable experience while dealing with various situations that come our way.

Learning to manage your window of tolerance can go a long way on your road to recovery from trauma, anxiety, or extreme stress. Recognize your window of tolerance and build awareness of your symptoms. By widening your Window of Tolerance, you are more likely reducing the change of leaving it.

Self-regulate when you are dysregulated and experience symptoms of hyper-arousal or hypo-arousal. Keep in mind that this takes continuous practice. There are no shortcuts to recover, and doing this once or twice will not permanently change your mental wellbeing.

Take things slowly and try to learn one thing at a time. Regularly practicing the tips and techniques mentioned will teach you to instinctively recognize your window of tolerance and to self-regulate when required. *Most importantly is to give yourself grace* when you work on making change and improving your mental health. Always know that you are worth it!

Practicing Mindfulness

1. ***Building Awareness***: Focusing your attention, identifying what you are feeling, asking yourself why you feel this way, and questioning why those feelings matter.

2. ***Be More Open:*** Let yourself feel everything. Be open to both positive and negatives, don't push away unpleasant thoughts or emotions, let negative thoughts/emotions flow and pass through your mind.

3. ***Be More Accepting:*** Accept feelings both positive and negative, and avoid judging or censoring of your thoughts and feelings. Don't be ashamed, rather embrace those thoughts and feelings.

4. ***Be Present:*** Stay in the present moment and focus on what you are currently doing. Pay attention without judgment, and avoid multitasking, as this is mentally draining.

5. ***Increase Happiness:*** There are four happiness chemicals that your brain releases when you feel good. These chemicals are known as DOSE. When you are happy and have a positive experience, your window of tolerance will naturally expand. By understanding how each of the chemicals works, you can trigger the release of one of the chemicals to improve your happiness. Here are some examples of activities you can do to get your

"Daily DOSE of Happiness"

When you feel good, your brain is releasing one of the happiness chemicals or happy hormones. There are four main happiness brain chemicals. Each chemical has a job to do and when your brain releases one of these chemicals, it helps you to feel good.

Dopamine: Make a to do list (each time you check off a task you increase dopamine levels), create something such as writing, music, arts and crafts, or practice meditation

Oxytocin: Physical touching, cuddling, hugging, and even eye contact, socializing with friends and family, listening to music

Serotonin: Spending time in the sunshine, taking cold showers, getting a massage

Endorphin: Laughter and crying, eating dark chocolate or spicy foods, creating music or art

Self-Regulation & It's Importance

Returning to the analogy of your window of tolerance being a river you are floating down self-regulation is an island along that river. When you start to feel uncomfortable and have difficulty staying afloat, you can stop and take a moment. This break gives you the opportunity to return to your window of tolerance. When you are not too far out of your Window of Tolerance, you have a better opportunity to self-regulate. The further outside you are, the more severe the symptoms will be which make it more difficult to self-regulate. This is why awareness is so important. It gives you the ability to identify your emotional state when you first begin to dysregulate. Being able to recognize your window of tolerance allows you to take action.

Being mindful helps to deal with undue stress and emotions by paying attention and staying in the present moment. It is not about stopping any unwanted stress or anxiety (unless it is in our control), but rather it is allowing those moments to pass without your body reacting in a negative way. You can practice mindfulness by practicing one or more of the following techniques:

Self-Regulate Hyperarousal. When you experience hyperarousal symptoms you can soothe yourself with one or more of the following strategies. If you are experiencing anger, release it by one or more of the following strategies. Also, if you are experiencing anger, release it by one or more of the following.

- Close your eyes and lay down to let yourself relax and calm down
- Give yourself a 10-second hug by wrapping your arms around yourself and holding tightly
- Stretch your arms out in front of you to relieve that tension build up
- Shake it off to relieve the stress
- Take a drink of water to cool yourself down and calm yourself

Self-Regulate Hypo-arousal. When you experience hypo-arousal symptoms, you can activate your body with these techniques. They is indicated by an individual who may go into freeze or collapse mode. On the outside they may appear withdrawn, quiet, hard to reach, emotionless, inactive, unproductive, and unable to learn. On the inside they may feel flat, disconnected, dead, shut down or numb.

Breathing exercises. These exercises allows to you calm your body and mind. Additional Techniques can be found later in the book.

Pause for a second

Take a long and slow deep breath

Inhale through your nose and fill your lungs

Hold the breath for four seconds

Exhale slowly through your mouth

Count each breath and do at least 10 deep breaths

It is important to choose the practices that fit the learning style and tolerance levels of the person who uses them. Sitting quietly and focusing on the breath for long periods of time may be soothing for some but very unsettling for others. If introducing mindfulness meditation, starting with very short periods of practice is the best approach. People can still benefit from only a few minutes of focusing their attention on their breath or their bodily sensations of sitting in the chair. For many people with trauma histories, other forms of mindfulness practices may be more helpful. For example, the trauma center headed by Dr. Bessel Van der Kolk, has developed a trauma sensitive yoga practice that has been used by adolescents and adults to manage symptoms.

Meditation/Mindfulness. Being mindful and meditating go hand in hand. Meditation helps to regulate emotions and thoughts, and relieves stress by calming you down. Additional techniques can be found later in the book. Studies show that practicing mindfulness helps people control their brains with greater ease, allowing them to put an end to anxious or traumatic thoughts. Mindfulness has been shown to be an effective stress reduction practice in general, but there may be other ways it works for people with C-PTSD & PTSD as well. Recent research suggests that mindfulness may help to mitigate the relationship between maladaptive thinking and posttraumatic distress. Over time, mindfulness meditation practice builds more connections s, go to www.traumacenter.org for studies supporting the application of yoga. One approach, which has been found particularly helpful, is a form of psychotherapy that combines mindfulness and experiential imagery, called Mindfulness Meditation Therapy (MMT). In this approach, the client is taught how to form a non-reactive relationship with his traumatic memory. The individual literally learns how to "sit" with the felt sense of the trauma, without becoming caught up in the contents. The purpose here is not to simply re-experience the traumatic memory and emotions, but to learn how to experience them differently. This Mindfulness Based Relationship creates a therapeutic space around the memory imagery and associated emotional energy that allows the client to gradually stop the secondary reactivity of resistance and avoidance. Now a new creative space is created which allows the emotions, which have been confined and frozen in place, to become malleable and change. This process of inner change leads to the eventual resolution and transformation of the trauma. In short, reactivity inhibits change, whereas mindfulness facilitates change and healing.

A central focus in MMT is to uncover this internal structure of the traumatic memory and then to investigate this experiential content. There is no attempt to interpret what arises, only to experience fully and know completely whatever arises. This process essentially de-constructs the emotional complex into smaller parts that the psyche can digest and integrate into more stable configurations that do not continue to generate emotional suffering. Of course, this requires considerable preliminary preparation so that the client can experience the internal imagery without becoming overwhelmed. Therefore, the preliminary phase of MMT is focused on establishing the Mindfulness Based Relationship (MBR) in which there is sufficient stability and non-reactivity to allow the imagery to unfold into present awareness. There are many approaches to achieve the right MBR, such as watching the imagery as if projected on a screen or placing the imagery at some distance in front. Through mindfulness and careful investigation, the client can discover for himself what works best for establishing the MBR. However, once a client begins to witness specific details about the imagery, he inevitably finds it much easier to observe the imagery without becoming reactive, because the specific structural details give him a specific focus, and this tends to prevent hyper-reactivity. The MBR is an essential part of the transformation process for many reasons, the primary reason being that it allows the compacted emotional complex to unfold into more manageable parts. At another level, the MBR allows the client to fundamentally change the way that he relates to his inner emotional experience and he begins to break free from seeing himself as a victim of the emotional trauma. This in itself is an essential requirement for change.

Practice Yoga. Yoga is the practice of controlling the mind and body. It helps improve your concentration, and reduces stress and helps to relieve any tension build up you may be experiencing. The core elements of yoga practice, such as breath work, postures, and meditation, help to equip youth with skills to handle **stress** and trauma-responses. A trauma-informed yoga practice can strengthen the mind and body connection, helping to reduce overstimulation and reactivity, and encourage relaxation. Preliminary research using a model of trauma-sensitive yoga, developed by the Trauma Center at the Justice Resource Institute in Brookline, Massachusetts, has shown a reduction in severity of PTSD symptoms and frequency of dissociative symptoms, and gains in vitality and body attunement [16], [35]. Trauma-sensitive yoga is different from other types of yoga in that the emphasis is on making individuals feel safe and giving them choices about how to execute their poses and even whether to attempt certain poses.

The meditative aspect of trauma-informed yoga "changes the way you react to triggers and gives you skills to manage physical or emotional symptoms that occur due to long-lasting trauma. Yoga may help with emotional stability and assist in changing your physiology so that physical symptoms are lessened. It gets you out of your amygdala, the part of the brain where a lot of your fear response is located. Instead, you're focusing on the here and now and using your pre-fontal cortex, so it's like you're moving away from the fear while being mindful." That doesn't mean individuals using a trauma-sensitive processes spend more time, or even as much time, as individuals in other yoga processes quietly meditating. Some trauma survivors may have a difficult time quietly meditating, but they needn't be silent and still to meditate. Yoga is meditation in motion.

Reduce Shame. It is common for everyone to experience shame from time to time. But if you are constantly feeling embarrassed and self-critical, it can be debilitating to your mental health. Here are five simple steps to help reduce shame:

- Name your shame
- Listen to how you speak to yourself
- Write about your shame
- Tell someone you trust about your feelings of shame
- Reframe it by using affirmations and self-compassion and self-love

Build Resilience. Resiliency is important for adapting in the face of adversity, trauma, tragedy, or stress. Building up your resilience will directly expand your window of tolerance and improve your ability to deal with difficult life experiences. The following are strategies for building resilience:

- Building connections
- Fostering wellness
- Finding purpose in life

Building connections refers to prioritizing relationships by connecting with those close to you. Join a group and build one-on-one relations. By *fostering wellness*, we focus on all three aspects of health (physical, mental, and social), not just one or two of them. We also want to avoid negative outlets (masking your pain with substance use/abuse).

Another way is to *find purpose in life*. We can do this by looking for opportunities for self-discovery, taking steps towards goals you have set (short- and long-term goals), embracing change and being optimistic. Also, by helping others (support a friend, volunteering, connecting with support groups) is a way to find purpose.

Activate your senses (tap into your five senses). This may include one or more of the following activities: taking a warm bath, having a massage, lighting aromatic candles or scents, playing music or natural sounds, and eating tasty food.

Grounding exercises. Take note of what you are feeling during an event. Hold an object in your hand and really focus on it. Close your eyes and take a few deep breaths, open your eyes, and look around the room and acknowledge 5 things you can see, 4 things you can feel, 3 things you can hear, 2 things you can smell, and 1 thing you can taste.

Physical activity. Engage in any form of physical exercise you enjoy.

Challenge your thoughts. Recognize negative thoughts and challenge the thoughts and reframe them in a positive way. *Write things down.* Writing helps clear your thoughts and unload all of your emotions; it also clears mental clutter and gives clarity and focus.

Panic Anxiety Stress Support Kit (PASS). Carry around with you a mental health first-aid kit. It will provide tips and tools for relieving anxiety and stress. It should be simple, easy to use, and provide access to useful strategies to alleviate your symptoms.

CHAPTER 3

YOUR BRAIN MATTERS

"Whispered your soft inner voice: To truly love yourself, you must em-brace everything you've learned on the journey, including lessons learned from making mistakes (being human)".

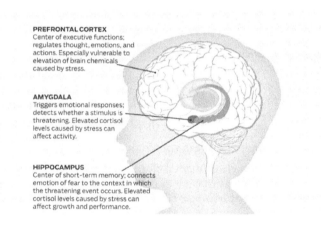

PREFRONTAL CORTEX
Center of executive functions; regulates thought, emotions, and actions. Especially vulnerable to elevation of brain chemicals caused by stress.

AMYGDALA
Triggers emotional responses; detects whether a stimulus is threatening. Elevated cortisol levels caused by stress can affect activity.

HIPPOCAMPUS
Center of short-term memory; connects emotion of fear to the context in which the threatening event occurs. Elevated cortisol levels caused by stress can affect growth and performance.

Anxiety is a normal human experience. Sometimes it can become too big, and when individuals get caught in the feeling of anxiety, it can affect their self-esteem, their engagement with the world, and the unfolding of their potential—but it does not have to be this way. Anxiety is manageable, and any important individual in a person's life can have profound capacity to empower the individual's ability to manage anxiety and move towards courage and resilience. With all anxiety comes opportunities to strengthen the mindset, skills and qualities that will lead them towards deeply fulfilling, brave, wholehearted living.

Research About Stress and the Brain - The Amygdala, Hippocampus, Pre-Frontal Cortex and Flashbacks

In a perfect world, stress would come with an adjustable dial. There would be 6-day weekends and coffee, beds and breakfasts would make themselves. We might not be able to stop the stress in our lives, but we can stop it causing ruin. Relationships, money, children, work and day-to- day stress means that it is not always possible to adjust the volume and intensity of stress in our life. What we can do is manage it, but tending to our own needs is often overlooked, and they almost never appear on our "must do" list. This is why I continue to stress the importance of self-care and how it can change the trajectory of one's life.

The Amygdala

When we look at stress and the brain, it has been found that exposure to chronic stress causes changes in the amygdala. These changes have been associated with anxiety and depression. The left hemisphere of the brain controls motor skills, language, memory creativity, details, sequence, and logical thoughts based on language. The right hemisphere controls emotional processing, memory retrieval, spatial manipulation, and facial recognition. Frontal lobe functions control impulse control, organization, time orientation, reading, and social cues. The amygdala region of the brain is primarily associated with emotional processing. It is specifically important when it comes to detecting fear and enables us to react (flight, flight, free, fawn). The amygdala is located in the medial temporal lobe, just in front of the hippocampus. This is a small almond shaped structure located deep in the middle of the temporal lobe. The amygdala is designed to detect threats in the environment and activate the fight or flight response; activate the sympathetic nervous system to help you deal with the threat; and help you store new emotional or threat-related memories. This is important for safety and survival. Sometimes however, the Amygdala sets off the alarm when there is no real danger and is now acting on a memory of a past traumatic event triggered by something in the immediate environment – a sound, smell, sight, or other sense. Our bodies are then flooded with adrenalin and we are needlessly prepared to react causing a potential buildup of the stress hormone cortisol.

After trauma, the amygdala can become even more highly attuned to potential threats in the environment, leading an individual to closely monitor their surroundings to make sure they are safe and have strong emotional reactions to people, places or things that might be threatening or that remind them of the trauma. This heightened attention to potential threats in the environment can make it hard for people to pay attention, go to new places or interact with people they do not know.

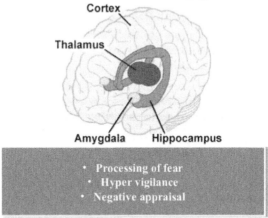

PTSD and the amygdala

Cortex

Thalamus

Amygdala   Hippocampus

- Processing of fear
- Hyper vigilance
- Negative appraisal

The Prefrontal Cortex

The *prefrontal cortex* is located in the frontal lobe just behind your forehead. The PFC is designed to regulate attention and awareness, and to make decisions about the best response to a situation, and determine the meaning and emotional significance of events, regulate emotions, and inhibit or correct dysfunctional reactions. The front part of the brain, known as the prefrontal cortex, is the rational part where consciousness lives, processing and reasoning occurs, and we make meaning of language. When a trauma occurs, people enter into a fight, flight, or freeze state, which can result in the prefrontal cortex shutting down. The brain becomes somewhat disorganized and overwhelmed because of the trauma, while the body goes into a survival mode and shuts down the higher reasoning and language structures of the brain.

The Prefrontal Cortex (PFC)

- Connected with the amygdala and exerts inhibitory control over stress responses and emotional reactivity; goals, reason, controls habits
- Prefrontal cortex actually shrinks with PTSD; children/adolescents/young adults don't have developed PFC
- Successful SSRI treatment restored PFC activation patterns

The Hippocampus

The Hippocampus works alongside the Amygdala and date stamps and logs our memories – a bit like a librarian. In a potentially traumatic situation however, the hippocampus is not as effect ad does to function at its best. It can be overwhelmed and log things in the wrong place with incorrect information which is why a memory of a traumatic time can feel as though it is happening again by way of intrusive thoughts, flashbacks and re-experiencing and hyper-arousal symptoms.

As stated above, the Hippocampus functions are interrupted in traumatized individuals, which results in impaired learning, less ability to create and retrieve memories (recall). Traumatized individuals often struggle with complex, goals directed behaviors, and have trouble adapting to transitions, changes and demands. The hippocampus is part of the limbic system in the brain that regulates emotional and behavioral responses. It is responsible for the ability to store and retrieve memories. As a result, individuals who experience trauma may not be able to retain information about how to tell if one situation is safe and another is dangerous, leading them to experience harmless situations as scary. Dr. Arielle Schwartz's 2016 article, "The Neurobiology of Trauma," describes the vital regions of the brain. The autonomic nervous system (ANS) plays a significant role in our emotional and physiological responses to stress and trauma. The ANS has two primary systems: *the sympathetic nervous system* and the *parasympathetic nervous system*. *The sympathetic nervous system* is associated with the fight or flight response and the release of cortisol throughout the bloodstream. *The parasympathetic nervous system* puts the brakes on the sympathetic nervous system, so the body stops releasing stress chemicals and shifts toward relaxation, digestion, and regeneration. The sympathetic and parasympathetic nervous systems are meant to work in a rhythmic alternation that supports healthy digestion, sleep, and immune system functioning. Dr. Schwartz goes on to describe how the "rhythmic balance" between the sympathetic and parasympathetic nervous systems becomes disrupted by chronic child abuse. This inability to synch the two functions leads to problems later. During an emotional flashback, because your ANS is damaged and uncoordinated, the amygdala recognizes what it perceives as danger (trigger) and reacts, triggering the fight/flight/freeze response. This reaction engages the sympathetic nervous system revving up your body and causing a significant amount of distress. However, unlike in normal circumstances, the parasympathetic nervous system does not engage in calming down the situation, leaving a person stranded in yesterday.

It is vital to remember that what is happening, the overstimulated ANS, the flashbacks, and the need for grounding techniques will not be a forever struggle. *One can heal from severe trauma.* Healing begins when one understands that they are not nor ever were responsible for what happened to them, and that it is now up to them to get better. One cannot go under, over, or around it. *The only way out is through.* There is no other way to achieve healing. Understanding why one can feel so bad and suffer from flashbacks is part of taking power away from the past and those who hurt you.

"Tell them it will take them longer to heal than what they want, but not as long as they fear." ~ Paula McNitt PhD

CHAPTER 4

"Trauma is a fact of life; it does not have to be a life sentence"

- Peter Levine

Flashbacks

Flashbacks in C-PTSD and PTSD occur when one relives a traumatic event while awake. Flashbacks are devastating to those who experience them, as they are suddenly and uncontrollably reliving something that happened in their past. Flashbacks are akin to vomiting when having a stomach virus. You cannot choose when or where it will happen. People experiencing flashbacks become transported back to the traumatic event, reliving it with all its sights, sounds, and fears as if it were happening in the present.

Emotional Flashbacks

Emotional flashbacks are a symptom of complex post-traumatic stress disorder, and they are different from what we have already discussed. They seem to be disconnected from the survivor's present reality, and include the triggering of emotions instead of the five senses. Emotional flashbacks are like having a *nightmare while you are awake.* Survivors experiencing emotional flashbacks are stranded in the feelings of being in danger, hopelessness, and helplessness that they felt at the time of the actual traumatic events. If, for example, the survivor as a child was physically traumatized, they certainly would have felt anger, rage, and hopelessness at the time. However, since they were only a helpless child, they could not escape or change their situation. As an adult, this same survivor's reaction might be triggered by a situation that somehow connects with those emotions, but instead of remembering the incident as in a flashback, they experience all the agonizing emotions that went along with the traumatic experience even though they are safe today in the present time.

C-PTSD and Emotional Flashbacks

The connection between complex post-traumatic stress disorder and emotional flashbacks is well-documented. The emotions that were ignored and stuffed away in childhood can be triggered back to life again, presenting disconnected emotions that seemingly come from nowhere.

One good example is a child who was emotionally abused daily by his family, telling him/her they were ugly and would never be anything. Although this child grew up to be a prosperous entrepreneur, they continued to experience feelings that they are ugly and an imposter in their accomplishments. Such feelings were triggered unexpectedly and abruptly and seemingly unconnected to their present reality.

The Experience of Having an Emotional Flashback

Emotional flashbacks are sudden and often prolonged regressions (amygdala hijackings) to the frightening and abandoned feeling-states of childhood. Emotional flashbacks happen with inappropriate and intense fight, flight or freeze instincts through the sympathetic nervous system. These instincts present intense and confusing periods of shame, fear, despair, and anger that are manifested against the survivor or those around them.

Often, when the survivors' primary emotion during an emotional flashback is fear, they feel panicky and overwhelmed. When the emotion of despair is dominant, it causes the survivor to feel numb, paralyzed, and feel that they need to hide. Such experiences typically come with toxic shame, which, as described in John Bradshaw's *Healing the Shame That Binds You (1988)*, toxic shame aids in the overpowering sense that the survivor is stupid, worthless, or flawed. Survivors often describe emotional flashbacks as feeling like something horrible is about to happen and that they must be on guard for any danger. It is an overwhelming sense that nuclear war is about to begin or that someone is going to die. The symptoms of emotional flashbacks are terrifying, extremely uncomfortable, and real for the survivor.

According to Peter Walker (psychotherapist) he offers the following definition of emotional flashbacks in his book *Complex PTSD: From Surviving to Thriving.*

"Emotional flashbacks are sudden and often prolonged regressions to the effect of being an abused/abandoned child. These feelings states can include overwhelming fear, shame, alienation, rage, grief, and depression. They also include unnecessary triggering of our fight, flight or freeze instincts".

Regression is a defense mechanism that awakens when survivors face anxiety-filled events that cause them to retreat to a childhood state. In regression, full-grown adults flashback back to their emotions as children and feel abandoned, abused, and helpless or overwhelming emotions of fear, rage, shame, depression, and grief that trigger a strong fight/flight/freeze/fawn response.

Flashbacks are considered one of the re-experiencing symptoms of C-PTSD. In a flashback, you may feel or act as though a traumatic event is happening again. A flashback may be temporary, and you may maintain some connection with the present or you may lose all awareness of what is going on around you and thus being taken back to your traumatic event.

 Individuals with CPTSD may also experience dissociation. Dissociation is an experience where you may feel disconnected from yourself and/or your surroundings. Similar to flashbacks, dissociation may range from temporarily losing touch with things that are going on around you, kind of like what happens when one may daydream, to having no memories for a prolonged period of time (or forever) and/or feeling as though you are outside of your body.

In coping with flashbacks and dissociation, *prevention* is key. Flashbacks and dissociation are often triggered or cued by some kind of reminder of a traumatic event. It is important to identify the specific things that may trigger flashbacks or dissociation. By knowing what your triggers are, you can either try to limit your exposure to those triggers or, if that is not possible, you can prepare for them by developing ways to cope with your reactions.

According to Peter Walker, survivors experiencing emotional flashbacks are overwhelmed with emotions they cannot understand or recognize with events they may or may not remember or connect these emotions to. Mr. Walker refers to 13 Steps to Managing and possibly overcoming Emotional Flashbacks.

Keep going, never, ever give up. Never. "It always seems impossible until it's done." ~ *Nelson Mandela*

13 Steps to Managing Emotional Flashbacks

- Say to yourself: "I am having a flashback". Flashbacks takes you into a timeless part of the psyche that makes you feel as helpless, hopeless, and surrounded by danger as when you were experiencing the trauma. The feels and sensations you are experiencing in flashbacks are memories that cannot hurt you now.

- **Remind yourself: "I feel afraid, but I am not in danger! I am safe now, here in the present".** Remember, you are now in the safety of the present, far from the danger of the past.

- **Own your right/need to have boundaries.** Remind yourself that you do not have to allow anyone to mistreat you, you are free to leave dangerous situations and protest unfair behavior.

- **Speak reassuringly to the Inner Child.** The child needs to know that you love them unconditionally and that they can come to you for comfort and protection when feeling lost and/or scared. Deconstruct the dark memories of childhood that were unrelenting. The unimaginable possibility of escaping the feelings of fear and abandonment is now imaginable.

- **Remember, the flashbacks will pass as it has many times before.** Remind yourself that you are in an adult body with the abilities, skills, and resources to protect yourself when you never were able to as a child. Feelings small and invisible can be a sign of a flashback. Ease back into your body. Fear launches one into "heady" worrying or numbing and spacing out.

- **Gently ask your body to relax.** Feel each of your major muscle groups and softly encourage them to relax. Breathe deeply, find a safe place to soothe yourself, and allow yourself to feel the fear without reacting to it.

- **Resist the inner critic's catastrophizing.** Use thoughts to stop the inner critic's endless exaggeration of danger and constant planning to control the uncontrollable. Refuse to shame, hate, or abandon yourself. Channel the anger of self-attacking into saying "NO" to unfair self-criticism. Use positive self-talk to replace negative thinking with a memorized list of your qualities and accomplishments.

- **Allow yourself to grieve.** Flashbacks are opportunities to release old, unexpressed feelings of fear, hurt and abandonment, and to validate and then soothe the child's experience of helplessness and hopelessness. Healthy grieving can turn your tears into self-compassion and your anger into self-protection.

- **Cultivate safe relationships and seek support.** Take time along when you need it, but do not let shame isolate you. Feeling shame does not mean you are shameful. Educate your loved ones and safe people about flashbacks, and ask them to help you talk and feel your way through them.

- **Learn to identify the types of triggers that lead to flashbacks.** Avoid unsafe people, places, activities, and triggering mental process. Practice prevention maintenance with these steps when triggering situations are unavoidable.

- **Figure out what you are flashing back to.** Flashbacks are opportunities to discover, validate, and heal old wounds from past abuse and abandonment. They also point to our still unmet developmental needs and can provide motivation to get them met.

- **Be patient with a slow recovery process.** It takes time to become un-adrenalized and considerable time to gradually decrease the intensity, duration, and frequency of flashbacks. Real recovery is a gradual progressive process (often two steps forward, one step back). Even with setbacks, know that you are still growing and recovering and do not be discouraged continue to love yourself through the process.

- **Do not be hard on yourself for having a flashback (Give yourself grace).** Flashbacks happen without your consent and certainly without you wanting them to occur. So, why be hard on yourself over something you have little control over? Again, it is important to give yourself grace. Emotional flashbacks are different from other type of flashbacks. The survivor experiencing it feels the emotions without physically reliving the incident. Emotional flashbacks are often part of the diagnosis of Complex-Post Traumatic Stress disorder. Dr. Peter Walker describes emotional flashbacks as sudden and often prolonged regressions into overwhelming "feelings-states" when a survivor experienced childhood abuse (Peter Walker, Complex-PTSD). Again, the emotions that accompany emotional flashbacks are overwhelming and can include fear, shame, alienation, grief, rage, and depression.

Additional strategies to assist with Emotional Flashbacks include:

- Keep a diary.
- Remind yourself that you are now an adult with allies, skills, and resources to protect you that you never had as a child.
- Own your right to have boundaries. Remind yourself that you do not have to allow anyone to mistreat you; you are free to leave dangerous situations.
- Find a safe place to unwind and soothe yourself. Wrap yourself in a blanket, hold a stuffed animal or other safe item, take a bath, take a nap.
- Resist the inner critics to catastrophizing situations
- Allow yourself to grieve. Flashbacks are opportunities to release old, unexpressed feelings of fear, hurt and/or abandonment.
- Cultivate safe relationships and seek support
- Be patient with a slow recovery process: it takes time in the present to become un-adrenalized.
- Be kind and give yourself grace
- Focus on your breathing. When you are frightened, you may stop breathing normally.
- Carry an object that reminds you of the present and focus on it.
- Tell yourself that you are safe and ground yourself in the present.
- Comfort yourself.
- Utilize other grounding techniques (see below)

Ways of Grounding

Grounding is a set of strategies that can help one detach from emotional pain (e.g., anxiety, anger, sadness, self-harm). It is a way to distract oneself by focusing on something other than the difficult emotions being experienced. You may also think of grounding as centering, distracting, creating a safe place, or healthy detachment.

There are three types of grounding. You can decide which one works better for you or if all are helpful.

1. Mental (focusing your mind)
2. Physical (focusing your senses)
3. Soothing (talking to yourself in a very kind way)
   - Mental Grounding Techniques
   - Describe your environment in detail, using all your senses (e.g., the walls are white, there are three blue chairs, there is a picture on the wall). In mental grounding you describe objects, sounds, textures, colors, smells, shapes, numbers, and temperature.
   - Play a "category" game. Try to think of types of dogs, cars, animals, songs, cities, sports, or famous people that begin with a letter or each letter of the alphabet.
   - Describe an everyday activity in great detail. For example, describe a meal that you cooked yesterday (e.g., First, I peeled the potatoes, and cut them into cubes, then boiled the water, added mayonnaise, mustard, salt, pepper, and eggs).
   - Count backwards from 100 by 5.

- Imagine. Use a pleasant or comforting mental image. Again, use all of your senses to make it as real and vivid as possible.
- Recite all of your family's names, their ages and one of their favorite activities.
- Read something, saying each work to yourself, or read each letter backwards so that you focus on the letters and not on the meanings of the words.
- Use humor. Think of something funny to jolt yourself out of your mood.
- Say a safety statement: I am safe right now. I am in the present, not in the past.
- Count to 10 or say the alphabet, very s…l…o…w…l…y.
- A calendar with the current month and year.

Physical Grounding Techniques

- Run cool or warm water over your hands.
- Grab tightly onto your chair as hard as you can; note the sensation and the experience.
- Touch various objects around you, a pen, your clothing, the table, the walls. Notice textures, colors, weigh, and temperature. Compare the objects you touch.
- Carry a grounding object in your pocket. A small object (a rock, ring, piece of cloth, squishy ball).
- Notice your body. The weight of your body in the chair; wiggling your toes in your socks; the feel of the back of the chair.
- Stretch. Extend your fingers, arms, legs as far as you can; slowly and gently roll your hands around.

- Clench and release your fists and repeat.
- Rub the palms of your hands together. Notice the sound and the feeling of warmth it brings.
- Eat something in a savoring way; fully experience the food; describe the sights, aromas, textures, flavors, and the experience in detail to yourself.
- Walk slowly, noticing each footstep, saying "left," "right" with each step.
- Focus on your breathing. Notice each inhale and exhale. Repeat a pleasant word to yourself with each exhale.
- Practice breathing techniques (progressive muscle relaxation and deep breathing).
- Hold a pillow or stuffed animal.
- Hold a piece of ice in your hand.
- Listen to music.
- Name 2 things you can see in the room with you.
- Name 2 things you can hear right now.
- Pay attention to the movement of your abdomen as you breathe.

Soothing Grounding

- Say positive statements, as if you were talking to a friend or child (e.g., You are a good person going through a difficult time. You'll get through this).
- Think of favorites. Think of your favorite color, animal, food, TV show, singer, artist, band.
- Picture people you care about and look at a photograph of them.

- Remember the words to an inspiring song, mantra, quotation, or poem that makes you feel better.
- Say a coping statement: "I can handle this," This feeling will pass."
- Plan a safe treat for yourself, such as a piece of fruit, a nice dinner, a warm bath.
- Remember a safe place and describe the sounds, colors, shapes, objects, smells, what you hear and textures.
- Think of things you are looking forward to in the next week, perhaps times with a friend, going to a move, taking a trip, going on a hike.
- A locket with a picture of someone important to you today.

Although grounding does not solve the problem that is contributing to the unpleasant emotions, it does provide a temporary way to gain control over your feelings and prevent things from getting worse. Grounding anchors you, gives you a chance to calm down, and allows you to eventually return and address the problem that is triggering the unpleasant emotions. Also, grounding can be done anytime, anywhere and one no one needs to know.

When you are overwhelmed with emotional pain you need a way to detach so that you can gain control over your feelings and feel safe. Grounding anchors you to the present reality. Many people with C-PTSD and PTSD struggle with either feeling too much (overwhelming emotions and memories) or too little (numbing and dissociation). In grounding, you achieve a balance between the two – conscious of reality and able to tolerate it.

Use grounding when you are faced with a trigger, having flashbacks, dissociating, having substance craving or when your emotional pain increases. Grounding puts healthy distance between you and these negative feelings.

Keep your eyes open, scan the room, and turn on the light to stay in touch with the present. Rate your mood before and after to test whether it worked. Before grounding, rate your level of emotional pain. Then re-rate your level of emotional pain after your grounding technique is implemented. Focus on the present, not the past or future. Note that grounding is not the same as relaxation techniques, however it can bring on a feeling of relaxation.

Using your 5 senses for grounding

- **Sight:** Take an inventory of everything around you. Connect with the present moment by listing everything around you. Identify all the colors you see. Count all the pieces of furniture around. List off all the noises you hear. Taking an inventory of your immediate environment can directly connect you with the present moment.

- **Smell:** Sniff some strong peppermint. When you smell something strong, it's very hard to focus on anything else. In this way, smelling peppermint can bring you into the present, slowing down or altogether stopping a flashback or an episode of dissociation.

- **Sound:** Turn on music. Loud, jarring music will be hard to ignore. As a result, your attention may be directed to that noise, bringing you into the present moment.

- **Taste**: Bite into a lemon or something else with a strong taste. The sourness of a lemon and the strong sensation it produces in your mouth when you bite into it can force you to stay in the present moment.

- **Touch**: Grip a piece of ice or another object with a strong sensation. If may be difficult to direct your attention away from the extreme coldness of the ice, forcing you to stay in touch with the present moment.

Practice! Practice! Practice! Like any other skills, grounding takes practice. Practice as often as possible and before you actually need it. Then, when you need to call upon your skill, you will have it know it and be able to call it up easily. Try to notice which method(s) are best for you. Physical, mental, or soothing grounding techniques or a combination of strategies. Try grounding for an extended amount of time (take as long as your body needs). Start grounding early on in a negative mood cycle. Start before the anger, anxiety or other feelings which make you feel out of control start to escalate. The sooner you begin your strategies, the easier it may be to return to your grounded state.

Additional grounding techniques:

If possible, say *out loud* the following questions (if you cannot speak out loud, then say them in your mind):

- Where am I?
- What is today?
- What is the date?
- What is the month?
- What is the year?
- How old am I?
- What season is it?

CHAPTER 5

"Like a tree, I flourish, and shed the leaves that are diseased".

Counseling/Therapy as treatment

Trauma-Informed Care understands and considers the pervasive nature of trauma and promotes environments of healing and recovery rather than practices and services that may inadvertently retraumatize. Trauma-Informed Care (TIC) is an approach in the human service field that assumes that an individual is more likely than not to have a history of trauma. Trauma-Informed Care recognizes the presence of trauma symptoms and acknowledges the role trauma may play in an individual's life- including service staff.

On an organizational or systemic level, Trauma-Informed Care changes organizational culture to emphasize respecting and appropriately responding to the effects of trauma at all levels. Similar to the change in general protocol regarding universal precautions. Trauma-Informed Care practice and awareness becomes almost second nature and pervasive in all service responses. Trauma-Informed Care requires a system to make a paradigm shift from asking, "What is wrong with this person?" to "What has happened to this person?" The intention of Trauma-Informed Care is not to treat symptoms or issues related to sexual, physical, or emotional abuse or any other form of trauma but rather to provide support services in a way that is accessible and appropriate to those who may have experienced trauma. When service systems operating procedures do not use a trauma-informed approach, the possibility for triggering or exacerbating trauma symptoms and re-traumatizing individuals increases.

A Trauma-Informed Care approach strives to understand the whole of an individual who is seeking services. When trauma occurs, it affects an individual's sense of self, their sense of others and their beliefs about the world. These beliefs can directly impact an individual's ability or motivation to connect with and utilize support services. A system utilizing a Trauma-Informed Care approach realizes the direct impact that trauma can have on access to services and responds by changing policies, procedures, and practices to minimize potential barriers. A system utilizing a Trauma-Informed approach also fully integrates knowledge about trauma into all aspects of services and trains staff to recognize the signs and symptoms of trauma and thus avoid any possibility of re-traumatization.

Counseling attempts to engage parts of the brain that have been dis-regulated and therefore are not able to resolve the trauma when people are in hyper-aroused or hypo-arousal states. According to Bessel Van Ker Kolk, "Traditionally we've tried to heal PTSD through talking and making meaning of the even. However. treatment methods that help calm arousal systems in the deeper regions of the brain have been helpful in calming C-PTSD more than those that try to do so through talking and reasoning". We call this "bottom-up" processing. Talk therapy works when the brain in "regulated" and functioning, but when the rational part of the brain is hijacked by the trauma memory, people may not hear words or reasoning or make meaning of events and experiences. When the deeper regions of the brain are in this state of distress, survivors are back in the trauma and their brain and body seem to go back in time.

Trauma-Informed Care follows five Guiding Principles that serve as a framework for how service providers and systems of care can work to reduce the likelihood of re-traumatization. These principles are generalizable across a variety of service settings. Rather than providing a set of practices and procedures, the principles can be interpreted and applied in ways that are appropriate for a specific type of service setting.

The Five Guiding Principles are safety, choice, collaboration, trustworthiness, and empowerment. Ensuring that the physical and emotional safety of an individual is addressed is the first important step to providing Trauma-Informed Care. Next, the individual needs to know that the provider is trustworthy. Trustworthiness can be evident in the establishment and consistency of boundaries and the clarity of what is expected in regard to tasks. Additionally, the more choice an individual has and the more control they have over their service experience through a collaborative effort with service providers, the more likely the individual will participate in services and the more effective the services may be. Finally, focusing on an individual's strengths and empowering them to build on those strengths while developing stronger coping skills provides a healthy foundation for individuals to fall back on if and when they stop receiving services.

Key Components of Trauma Informed Care are Incorporating the approach to every aspect of the organization, creating a genuine culture change. Demonstrating greater awareness of the impact of trauma on all individuals served by the program, organization, or system, including its own workforce. An acceptance that trauma influence the effectiveness of all human services (care coordination, medical care, criminal justice, etc.) (SAMSHA, 2015). Solution-based service approach. Recognizing the pervasiveness of trauma. Changing the thinking from "What is wrong with this individual?" to "What happened to this individual?" "Involves vigilance in anticipating and avoiding institutional processes and individual practices that are likely to retraumatize individuals who already have a trauma history". Staff at all levels change their behaviors, actions, and policies in keeping with a Trauma Informed Care approach (Jennings, 2004).

A trauma-informed approach can guide therapy to help clients see their critical or isolating parts from a new angle. By exploring them instead of rejecting them, the self-understanding and compassion needed for friendships and relationships can grow stronger. Therapy can be a truly emotionally corrective relationship, where the client learns that having a witness accept their feelings and history can allow them to feel safer than ever before! Trauma creates an urgent need to protect. To a person with a traumatic history, a barrier to connection is like a life preserver, since he/she believes that disconnection keeps them safe, and validates a person's need for safety. Instead of criticizing themselves for their barriers, clients can explore what is blocking them. For example: "Is there a self-protector part inside you who says: "I am going to withdraw and stay safe, so you don't hurt me?" In addition, trauma-informed therapy can offer clients a vision of what healthy connections look like. For example, they can experience feeling supported, heard, and affirmed.

No relationship is perfect, but misunderstandings do not have to hurt forever. When something injures a healthy relationship, we address it. We want to clear it up. We want to heal the injury. In doing so, in the therapeutic relationship we create what therapists call a *corrective emotional experience*. When clients experience relationship trauma, particularly as children, they often learn to "put up and shut up" as a go-to coping skill. But this creates other problems later in life. Hiding hurts, and withdrawing from a relationship when discomfort surfaces preempts the opportunity to heal misunderstandings. Trauma survivors often become adults without the experience of having relationship repair tools. Sometimes, disconnects happen in therapy. Dr. Suzanne LaCombe calls them **mis-attunements.** Healing mis-attunements is enormously valuable. Therapy can provide vital healing experiences by encouraging safety and trust and providing positive results when a client brings up feeling bad about something that happened during a session.

1. Witnessing feedback about our own insensitivity, when clients are brave enough to share that something the therapist said or did, did not sit well with them, doesn't mean one is not a good therapist. Healing this rift can be a huge therapeutic strength as LaCombe explains. When the therapist cares enough to respond to hurt feelings with understanding, an apology or clarification for a client, they are creating the uplifting healing experience of relationship repair. Maybe for the first time in their lives, they see how a painful disconnect can become a point of healing and deeper reconnection. Corrective emotional experiences can transform a maladaptive idea such as "suck it up" into a useful tool for further healing, such as "speak up," first inside the safety of therapy, and later, in healthier relationships outside of therapy. Therapist can help clients learn that having healthy relationships can repair even old emotional wounds.

2. In a healthy relationship with yourself, you can question unrealistic standards you may be holding yourself to and soothe self-criticism with compassion. A healthy therapeutic relationship can help clients see different parts of themselves. The therapist can witness where they seem strong, where they seem weaker, and be curious about how these parts might relate (or integrate) in a more compassionate way. Curiosity is a powerful therapeutic tool that can be offered to trauma survivors. For example, therapists can encourage client's to think about how their inner world may actually contain different parts, with different abilities and needs. Clients may more easily recognize the adult, the part they hold accountable, the part that takes responsibility. They may readily see a harsh critical advisor. But what about their more tender human need for emotional connection? What about the part(s) that hurt, such as a scared inner child? The same adult who would offer compassion to another person can learn to extend this same support to the child or hurt place inside. By encouraging curiosity about nurturing rather than criticizing parts of themselves, we can help clients use new resources to feed the wise adult parts. They can then learn to help hurt parts heal and grow.

3. Consider the opportunity for secure attachment in the current relationships they have been able to develop as an adult.

Trauma survivors may have experienced relationships as unsafe places to open up. However, that may not be true of current relationships. It takes encouragement and intention to explore unknown parts of a current relationship. As therapists, we can witness what we notice about the strengths and potential capacity for support and love in our clients. We can witness or be curious about what a client expects from a current relationship. For example, the therapist can ask if they expect to be a giver, accepting nothing in return. Therapy can support a client in appreciating/evaluating the nature of the relationship he or she actually has, how to find resources for self-nurture and support, and the real opportunity for healing in secure attachment in their current relationships. At first, it may feel strange or even risky to see the true depth of the love, support, and compassion that caring friends or family members can and want to provide. A real chance for greater emotional connection, safety, and security may be closer than our clients think. The awareness to look at relationships objectively and consider this potential is beneficial for the client. Allowing the heart to be open to compassion, support, and deeper relationships and asking for help can be especially difficult for those who have survived trauma. Learning to allow the heart to open takes courage, time, and responsive, compassionate support. Through trauma-informed therapy, it is possible to help people realize that they truly do deserve deep relationships as they grow and change through life—in the good times and the hard times.

There can be tremendous healing that comes from repairing wounds in therapeutic relationships.

Shame in Trauma

CPTSD unlocks an entire array of negative emotions, including fear, anger, anxiety, and sadness. These emotions are entirely justified for anyone who has had a traumatizing experience, and over time they will likely begin to fade as healing takes place. But there is one emotion that tends to remain after a traumatic event that significantly hinders the recovery process. This intense emotion is shame.

Shame is a uniquely destructive emotion that anyone can face in their life. What makes shame such a strong feeling is that it damages a person's self-image. Shame and guilt are two separate emotions. On occasion the two have been interchanged. However, shame is a negative self-judgement, viewing oneself as worthless or less than. Whereas, with guilt one may evaluate an action or behavior they did as unfavorable, yet as a person you may still feel internally valued.

Shame is a painful, universal emotional response to a failure, shortcoming, or other wrongdoing of what society demands or what a person demands of him or herself. Scientists have learned that very young infants experience shame (as a personal feeling of unworthiness) when they experience rejection—even if it is unintentional. Shame is particularly challenging because once it has formulated, it can be very difficult to free oneself of it. In fact, many people tend to be so shame-bound that they retreat from the world around them, not allowing resources to help them get back to a healthier mindset that allows them to acknowledge their self-worth.

Shame is one of the most corrosive human emotions. It can make people think that they are failures, that they don't belong, or that the trauma they experienced was their fault. None of that is true, but the inner voice can be very convincing and hard to ignore.

Children, who are admonished for doing something over which they have limited or no control, are also capable of feeling shame.

On a more serious, long-lasting scale, physical and sexual abuse, and other traumatic experiences, particularly those that happen directly to the child without adequate intervention, may lead to the development of shame as well (J. Ungvarsky, *Shame*).

Identifying the origin of the shame-wound is critical as well. If one is the child of abusive and/or addicted parents, their shame could have been an emotional and psychological 'transplant.' Assessing if the shame is a consequence of actions, inactions, or someone else's conflicts, can allow for internal conflict resolution. Based on the extensive research and data available, psychologists believe that shame cultivates the need for approval from others. Shame can result when a person senses or experiences that someone disapproves of them or something about them. Shame can result when a person actually did something shameful, like doing harm or damage to a person, their property, or to animals. A person can also experience shame as an adult when something happens that they have little or no control over (Ungvarsky, *Shame*).

Shame is one of CPTSD's signature features, and it belongs to the cluster of emotional dis-regulation symptoms. Feeling of shame is rooted in the false belief that one is inherently bad and has a negative sense of self as someone unworthy, disgusting, or damaged.

The distress caused by shame can be inspired by both positive and negative cognition and motivation. The thinking that supports socially acceptable behaviors, like dressing appropriately, keeping one's work area neat and clean, and not littering, are examples of positive cognition utilized to avoid shame. The motivation is a positive and necessary one, and any well-functioning society will have citizens motivated by a healthy degree of shame. The unhealthy side of shame is if the thinking that results from other's disapproval becomes a crushing and sweeping feeling self-worthlessness. Some typical examples of shame related beliefs are:

- I don't matter
- I don't deserve anything nice
- I am a fraud
- I am a failure
- I shouldn't have been born
- I am defective/There is something wrong with me
- I am bad
- I am stupid
- I am an emotional wreck
- I am damaged goods
- I am broken

This toxic shame may have its roots in chronic exposure to conditions that cause shame. Conditions, events, or circumstances that cause a person to question their value can cause shame. Shame can also be triggered by failures or disappointments, and it does not necessarily have to be rooted in childhood trauma. The way that shame feels depends on the person experiencing it, and on the cognition that is involved.

People with CPTSD often find themselves gripped by intense feelings of shame that debilitate them and trap them in a cycle of despair. Intense and uncontrollable feelings of shame can be a major obstacle to recovery. This may prevent one from being able to control what has happened in the past. However, addressing feelings of shame is a necessary part of the healing process.

Strategy 1: The next time you feel the urgent need for someone's approval, stop, breathe, and do nothing. Pay attention to everything that is going on. Try to ride out the wave for approval seeking, and then appreciate yourself for meeting the challenge head-on!

Strategy 2. When you encounter a situation that you normally judge, criticize, or reject yourself for, do the exact opposite! Write yourself a note of appreciation, and drop it in a jar, for success measurement. Let those notes pile up as you teach your inner child the joys of celebrating growth and challenges met with dignity!

Other manifestations of shame can be shyness and self-consciousness, especially when a person is fearful of doing something that might cause embarrassment. Some psychologists consider bullying as an externalization of one's unresolved feelings of shame and inadequacy. When someone has the feeling that nothing, they do is correct nor meets the needs and expectations of others, that person has an inferiority complex. Most psychologists will attest to an inferiority complex as the most severe display of shame. Withdrawal in many ways to avoid any disapproval is a typical coping mechanism with this form of shame (Ungvarsky, *Shame*)

Strategy 3: Challenge yourself for the next 24 hours to instantly replace any negative self-condemnation with one realistic, positive thing you enjoy about being you! That will be your focus, your new best friend, who speaks only the truth to you. *Remember: self-judgment is not the same thing as honest self-appraisal and examination. It is just the opposite, as it fuels the obsessive-compulsive need to torment oneself needlessly, and without merit.*

Another major adaptation of unresolved shame is that shame-based people tend to keep secrets. Maintaining a secret vault, sealed off by shame, comes at a price to one's well-being. Secrecy is known to be interrelated with depression, anxiety, and poor physical health. The disguise of secrecy causes distraction, loneliness, disconnect, and places a barrier to true intimacy with others (Slepian, Kirby, & Kalokerinos, 2019).

It is pertinent to the discussion of shame and emotions, to specify that shame is a self-conscious emotion. As a self-conscious emotion, shame has more important consequences for secrecy, dissimilar to more basic emotions, like anger and fear for example. This is because basic emotions like anger, fear, or joy, can denote to external targets. Emotions that are of the self-conscious variety, center on the self, therefore, secrets often entail negative self-relevant information. Consequently, negative self-conscious emotions—stimulated through contemplation on how an event is relevant to self-representations —are most likely to fuel ongoing shame (Slepian, Kirby, & Kalokerinos, *Shame, Guilt and Secrets*). In mapping out shame and relevant guilt, it is helpful to note that these emotions reside in the private self. The private self contains one's secrets, in contrast to embarrassment, for example, which refers to the public self. Shame-related emotions are frequently associated with moral reasoning, and secrets usually contain moral violations (Tracy et al., 2007).

Strategy 4: Draw out a map of where your shame hides out. Be as detailed as you can. Write a love-letter to your shame and drop it off in a hiding place. Congratulations! You have taken a huge step towards extending empathy, forgiveness, and love to a part of yourself that needs your open embrace.

Please know that shame is an emotion that can be controlled. A healthy approach to controlling emotions includes sufficient self-awareness of emotional triggers and practicing appropriate coping skills. Without a decision to be self-aware, have good impulse control, and regular self-assessment, emotions will take over. Shame can be triggered when feeling stressed, angry, in love, or other emotions that involve our self-worth. Overall, people want to feel valued, with self-worth, and worthy of love and belonging. There are situations that we do not have control over our in environment, but we can be good stewards of our thoughts.

It is advisable to live in, and continually co-create an environment that is supportive, healthy, and "other-centered." Shame and guilt thrive in environments that are self-centered, critical, intolerant, or abusive. Building a reservoir of positive life actions to increase self-esteem as a buffer for shame, involves a supportive environment that begins with one's thoughts. Practicing patience is critical to the process of healing shame, reducing the intensity of triggers, and choosing healthy responses when triggered.

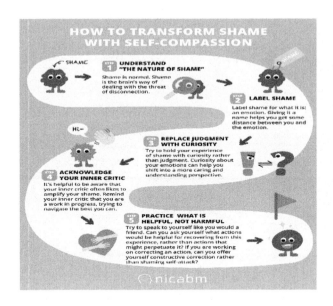

The Compass of Shame

Withdrawal

· Isolating Oneself
· Running & Hiding

*Looks like a classical shame response:
Feeling rejected, distanced, isolated &
Humiliated & withdrawing from connection.

*Head & neck slump, eyes droop & turn away,
Upper body goes limp ~ collapses

*Don't want to be out with people/ Withdraw into self/
Get quiet/ Space out/ Depression

Attack Self

· Self Put Down
· Masochism

*The ways one insults the self in internal dialogs
(our Critic) or in presenting one's self to others.

*Self-talk - "I'm unworthy, lack value, defective, stupid, etc."

*Offer self to others in demeaning sexual/ physical relationships
& allow the other to feel powerful & have more value.
This behavior pattern can manage the
loneliness of withdrawal but creates emotional pain.

*Manages shame by creating emotional pain.

Attack Other

· Turning the Tables
· Blaming the Victim
· Lashing out Verbally or Physically

*Establishing immediate proof that one is more powerful,
bigger, stronger, meaner than someone else.
*Diminishing someone else so one doesn't feel one's own
diminishment.

Bantering to "reduce"   →   Insults, abuse
the other   violence, cruelty

Avoidance

· Denial
· Abusing Drugs & Alcohol
· Distraction Through Thrill Seeking

Strategies to turn off the bad feeling:
*Addictive &/or compulsive behaviors, e.g. drinking, drug use,
compulsive overeating, compulsive spending.

*Act out in 'shameless' ways ~ "I'll show you who's bad ...."

*OVER work, OVER do, OVER give, OVER strive.
Emphasize those things that bring you pride, affirmation, compliments, approval.
Ignore the situations that make you feel bad or less than....
& pursue its opposite.

CHAPTER 6

MOVING FORWARD INTO HEALTHIER RELATIONSHIPS

"Trauma creates changes you don't choose. Healing is about creating change that you do choose."

Entering a Healing Relationship can be a Challenge for Trauma Survivors and those experiencing C-PTSD

It is good, healthy, and human to want love and to seek it out. We live longer, healthier lives when we feel close to someone safe. Some people feel painfully disconnected, and long to open up to others, but they stop themselves from reaching out. As therapists, we want to empower people to build more meaningful connections. For all of us, a healthy relationship matters. In fact, deep healthy relationships are essential to life. For trauma survivors, the act of deepening relationships in a healthy way can be particularly difficult. Well-meant urging or pressure to reach out in a time of need does not work for those who have experienced trauma. Something seemingly simple like accepting a compliment may be painfully hard. But the ability to integrate these fears and hesitations is crucial to your work to live a fuller, more balanced life.

Living through traumatic events may result in expectations of danger, betrayal, or potential harm within new or old relationships. Survivors may feel vulnerable and confused about what is safe, and therefore it may be difficult to trust others, even those whom they trusted in the past. It may feel frightening to get close to people for fear of being hurt in an unsafe world. Or people may feel angry at their helplessness and the loss of control in their lives, and become aggressive or try to control others. Anger and aggression may also arise because, after traumatic experiences, a person may feel threatened very easily. This defensive aggression is a natural reaction for a person who feels threatened. An individual's sense of who he or she is may also be affected. Trauma survivors may feel intense shame, unlovable or bad in some way, or guilty about what happened to them or about something that they did or feel that they should have done in the traumatic situation. A person may feel that no one can truly understand what has occurred, or may worry that it is a burden to discuss these experiences within a close relationship. For some it becomes natural to isolate from others, withdrawing from friends, family, coworkers, and life, feeling distant, disconnected, or detached. Others may become anxious or frightened in relation to others, experience them as having power or control, or easily feel abandoned or rejected. Still others may become overprotective or dependent. Many trauma survivors feel emotionally numb and have trouble feeling or expressing positive emotions in a relationship. Also, physical intimacy may be more difficult, and some survivors of traumatic experiences may find it difficult or impossible to have a fulfilling sexual relationship. Some people experience many of these feelings, which can be confusing or frightening.

Here are some strategies that can help people explore. Rather than criticizing themselves for their struggle to connect with others, these strategies are tools to help them connect. There are good reasons trauma survivors resist forming deeper relationships. It may feel impossible to become vulnerable enough (and feel safe) to admit what they want or need, let alone to share it. For them, self-imposed isolation has become a way to cope:

- Some feel they should hunker down and handle their struggles themselves.
- Some tell themselves, "Nobody will get it."
- Often, trauma survivors feel ashamed or weak—undeserving of support or compassion.
- For some, it is the only way they have felt somewhat safe in the past—being alone!

C-PTSD is a serious medical condition. It is vital for a partner to know that it is not a choice and not something that another person can cure. Strong relationships are important for everyone's well-being, and negative relationships can make recovery from CPTSD more difficult. Supporting a partner may give them the space they need to pursue recovery, while offering reassurance can remind them that someone loves them and is there for them. To help a partner with C-PTSD, a person can:

- Avoid blaming them for their symptoms, minimizing the severity of their trauma, and telling them to "snap out of it."
- Encourage them to seek treatment and offer to help them do so.
- If the partner has thoughts of suicide, work with a therapist to develop a suicide prevention plan. Remove any weapons from the house.

- Encourage the loved one to talk about their feelings if they want, but avoid forcing them to do so.
- Do not tell them how to feel or give unsolicited advice.
- Recognize the effect of C-PTSD on the relationship, but do not blame all of its problems on C-PTSD.
- Identify the other person's triggers and work to minimize their exposure to them. For example, if loud noises or voices are a trigger, avoid leaving the television on.
- Talk about ways to minimize the effect of C-PTSD on the relationship. For example, some people with C-PTSD may fear abandonment, so making threats to leave may intensify their symptoms and make conflict worse.
- Be sensitive and empathetic to their emotions. Offer comfort and warmth, especially during flashbacks or times of intense anxiety.

Trauma survivors and their partners have different needs for support. How can one respond when the other is grappling with mental health issues? How do you calm things down when overwhelming emotions get triggered? It may take therapy for couples to find answers that are most healing for them. But some general tips for trauma survivors and their partners that can help are:

Have a really good support system for each of you and the relationship. Make time for family and friends who are positive about your relationship and respect you and your loved one.

Find a trauma-informed therapist to guide you as a couple or as individuals in your effort to better understand yourselves and each other.

Find resources outside of therapy such as support groups or other similar activities

Take time for psychoeducation. Learn about the nature of trauma, self-care, and healing techniques like mindfulness.

Treatment is available to respond to these difficult experiences, minimize isolation, and restore a sense of hope. It can be helpful to discuss traumatic experiences, feelings of grief, and relationship difficulties with a professional who is familiar with the complex effects of trauma. A therapist can offer a safe relationship for building trust and a sense of security. The opportunity within that relationship to establish meaning, purpose, and hope can be a first step in developing or reestablishing relationships with others and with oneself, building a social network of support, and engaging more fully with life. Learning how to manage communication helps couples restore calm and provide comfort as their understanding of trauma grows. For example, couples can utilize the follow statements to help in communication:

Use self-observation to recognize when to slow down or step back as feelings escalate

Practice mindfulness to raise awareness and recognize triggers for each of you

Develop some phrases to help you stay grounded in the present and re-direct your dialog, such as:

1. "I wonder if we can slow this down.
2. "It seems like we're getting triggered by this. Can we figure out what's going on with us?"

3. "I wonder if we are heading into an area that is not focused on the here and now."
4. "I'm thinking this could be something we should talk about in therapy."
5. "I wonder if we could try and stay focused on what is going on for us – is that possible?"

Communication can also help a partner comfort a loved one during a flashback. Techniques include:

- Reminding the person that he or she is safe.
- Calling attention to the here and now (referencing the present date, location and other immediate sights and sounds).
- Offering a glass of water, which can help stop a flashback surprisingly well. (It activates the salivary glands, which in turn stimulates the behavior-regulating prefrontal cortex.)

Healing childhood wounds takes careful, hard work. But it is possible to replace old rules bit by bit. Finding a therapist who can recognize and acknowledge the hurt, which the survivor has carried alone for so long, is key to repairing deep wounds. Partners may decide to work individually with their own trauma-informed therapist, while working with another as a couple, to provide the resources they need. When a survivor of trauma can finally find comforting connection with a therapist, and then with their partner, the relationship between the couple can begin to support deep healing as well. The more we understand about the impact of trauma, the more we can help those touched by it to go beyond surviving, and find the healing security of healthier loving relationships.

The Relationship Spectrum

Relationships can range from healthy to abusive, and some relationships may be unhealthy, but not abusive. Here's a breakdown of the relationship spectrum:

A Healthy Relationship	An Unhealthy Relationship	An Abusive Relationship
A healthy relationship means that both you and your partner are...	An unhealthy relationship starts when just one of you...	An abusive relationship starts when just one of you...
1) Communicating You talk openly about problems without shouting or yelling. You listen to one another, hear each other out, respect each other's opinions, and are willing to compromise.	**1) Not communicating** Problems are not talked about at all. You don't listen to each other or try to compromise.	**1) Communicates abusively** During disagreements there is screaming, cursing, or threatening, or these things happen even when there is no argument. A partner is demeaning or insulting toward the other.
2) Respectful You value each other as you are. Culture, beliefs, opinions and boundaries are valued. You treat each other in a way that demonstrates the high esteem you hold for one another.	**2) Disrespectful** One or both partners are inconsiderate toward the other. One or both partners don't treat each other in a way that shows they care.	**2) Is disrespectful through abuse** A partner intentionally and continuously disregards your feelings and physical safety.
3) Trusting You both trust each other, and the trust has been earned.	**3) Not trusting** There is suspicion that your partner is doing things behind your back, or your partner is suspicious of your loyalty without any reason.	**3) Falsely accuses the other of flirting or cheating** A partner suspects flirting or cheating without reason and accuses the other, often harming their partner verbally or physically as a result.
4) Honest You are both honest with each other but can still chose to keep certain things private. For example, you both know that it is important to be honest about things that affect or involve the relationship and still know that it is also o.k. to keep certain things private.	**4) Dishonest** One or both partners are telling lies to each other.	**4) Doesn't take responsibility for the abuse** The violent or verbally abusive partner denies or minimizes their actions. They try to blame the other for the harm they're doing.
5) Equal You make decisions together and you hold each other to the same standards.	**5) Trying to take control** One or both partners sees their desires or decisions as more important. One partner is or both partners are focused only on getting their own way.	**5) Controls the other partner** There is no equality in the relationship. What one partner says goes, and if the other partner tries to change this there is increased abuse.
6) Enjoy Personal Space You both enjoy spending time apart and respect when one of you voices a need for space.	**6) Feeling smothered or forgetting to spend time with others** So much time is spent together that one partner is beginning to feel uncomfortable. Or sometimes both partners spend so much time together that they ignore friends, family or other things that used to be important to them.	**6) Isolates the other partner** One partner controls where the other one goes, who the other partner sees and talks to. The other partner has no personal space and is often isolated from other people altogether.

INSTRUCTIONS: Give an example from real life or make up a story about a couple in one of these relationships where all six of the traits are mentioned.

CHAPTER 7

"Healing doesn't have to look magical or pretty. Real healing is hard, exhausting and draining. Let yourself go through it. Don't try to paint it as anything other than what it is. Be there for yourself with no judgement."

Post Traumatic Growth (PTG)

In the mid-90s, psychologist Richard Tedeschi, PhD, and Lawrence Calhoun, PhD, developed the PTG theory that people who endure psychological struggle following adversity can often see positive growth afterward. They coined the term post-traumatic growth at the University of Carolina, and defined it as a positive psychological change in the wake of struggling with highly challenging life circumstances (Tedeschi and Calhoun, 2004). It asserts that human beings can be changed by their encounters with life challenges, sometimes in radically positive ways. People who undergo post-traumatic growth flourish in life with a greater appreciation and more resilience. Posttraumatic Growth is both a process and an outcome: The experience of positive changes in oneself as a result of the struggle with traumatic events. Resilience is "The ability to recover readily from illness, depression, adversity or the like." The ability to regain shape. Also, resistance to adversity. Versus PTG is a new level of functioning and perspective-transformative responses to adversity. Primary vehicle is cognitive processing of the shattered assumptive world.

PTG involves life-altering and favorable psychological changes that can potentially change the way one perceives the world. It comes with a new understanding of life, relationships, money, success, and health. PTG tends to occur in five general areas. (1.) Sometimes people who must face a major life crisis develop a sense that new opportunities have emerged from the struggle, opening up possibilities that were not present before. (2.) A second area is a change in relationships with others. Some people experience closer relationships with specific people, and they can also experience an increased sense of connection to others who suffer. (3.) A third area of possible change is an increased sense of one's own strength: "If I lived through that, I can face anything" type of thinking. (4.) A fourth aspect of posttraumatic growth experienced by some is a greater appreciation for life in general. (5.) The fifth area involves the spiritual or religious domain. Some individuals experience a deepening of their spiritual lives, which can involve a significant change in one's belief system. Tedeschi and Calhoun found that firmly held religious and philosophical beliefs are often questioned following traumatic events.

1. Embracing new opportunities – both at the personal and the professional fronts.
2. Improved personal relationships and increased pleasure derived from being around people we love.
3. Increased emotional strength and resilience.
4. A heightened sense of gratitude toward life altogether.
5. Greater spiritual connection.

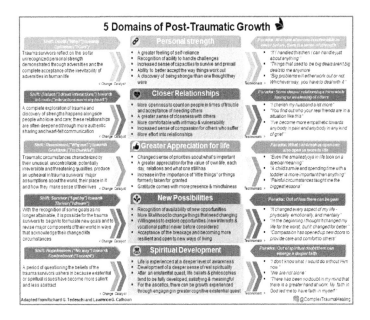

No relationship is perfect, but misunderstandings do not have to hurt forever. When something injures a healthy relationship, we address it. We want to clear it up. We want to heal the injury. In doing so, in the therapeutic relationship we create what therapists call a *corrective emotional experience.* When clients experience relationship trauma, particularly as children, they often learn to "put up and shut up" as a go-to coping skill. But this creates other problems later in life. Hiding hurts, and withdrawing from a relationship when discomfort surfaces preempts the opportunity to heal misunderstandings. Trauma survivors often become adults without the experience of having relationship repair tools. Sometimes, disconnects happen in therapy. Dr. Suzanne LaCombe calls them **mis-attunements.** Healing mis-attunements is enormously valuable. Therapy can provide vital healing experiences by encouraging safety and trust and providing positive results when a client brings up feeling bad about something that happened during a session.

1. **Witnessing feedback about our own insensitivity, when clients are brave enough to share that something we said or did, did not sit well with them, doesn't mean are not a good therapist.** Healing this rift can be a huge therapeutic strength as LaCombe explains. When we care enough to respond to hurt feelings with understanding, an apology or clarification to a client, we are creating the uplifting healing experience of relationship repair. Maybe for the first time in their lives, they see how a painful disconnect can become a point of healing and deeper re-connection. Corrective emotional experiences can transform a maladaptive idea such as "suck it up" into a useful tool for further healing, such as "speak up," first inside the safety of therapy, and later, in healthier relationships outside of therapy. We can help clients learn that having healthy relationships can repair even old emotional wounds.

2. **In a healthy relationship with yourself, you can question unrealistic standards you may be holding yourself to and soothe self-criticism with compassion.** A healthy therapeutic relationship can help clients see different parts of themselves. We can witness where they seem strong, where they seem damaged, and be curious about how these parts might relate (or integrate) in a more compassionate way. Curiosity is a powerful therapeutic tool we can offer trauma survivors. For example, we can encourage them to think about how their inner world may actually contain different parts, with different abilities and needs. Clients may more easily recognize the adult, the part they hold accountable, the part that takes responsibility. They may readily see a harsh critical advisor. But what about their

more tender human need for emotional connection? What about the hurt parts, such as a scared inner child? The same adult who would offer compassion to another person can learn to extend this same support to the child or hurt place inside.

By encouraging curiosity about nurturing rather than criticizing parts of themselves, we can help clients use new resources to feed the wise adult parts. They can then learn to help hurt parts heal and grow.

3. Consider the opportunity for secure attachment in the current relationships they have been able to develop as an adult.

Trauma survivors may have experienced relationships as unsafe places to open up. However, that may not be true of current relationships. It takes encouragement and intention to explore unknown parts of a current relationship. As therapists, we can witness what we notice about the strengths and potential capacity for support and love in our clients. We can witness or be curious about what a client expects from a current relationship. For example, we can ask if they expect to be a giver, accepting nothing in return. Therapy can support a client in appreciating/evaluating the nature of the relationship he or she actually has, how to find resources for self-nurture and support, and the real opportunity for healing in secure attachment in their current relationships. At first, it may feel strange or even risky to see the true depth of the love, support, and compassion that caring friends or family members can and want to provide. A real chance for greater emotional connection, safety, and security may be closer than our clients think. The awareness to look at relationships objectively and consider this potential is beneficial for the client. Allowing the heart to be open to compassion, support, and deeper relationships and asking for help can be especially difficult for those who have survived trauma. Learning to allow the heart to open takes courage, time, and responsive, compassionate support. Through trauma-informed therapy, it is possible to help people realize that they truly do deserve deep relationships as they grow and change through life—in the good times and the hard times.

Not everyone who undergoes trauma experiences post-traumatic growth. Individual responses and emotional perception of the damage guides the way they adapt and learn in the long run. Some studies have shown that almost 90% of trauma victims have experienced at least one aspect of post-traumatic growth after a stressful encounter (Calhoun & Tedeschi, 1990). *Generally speaking, post-traumatic growth is a positive indicator of recovery and healthy coping.* While the grief may still be there, post-traumatic growth allows one to look forward in life instead of being stuck in the past.

C-PTSD & Resilience

The Importance of Self Care

Self-Care is Self-Love

While the DSM-5 (2013) recognizes these symptoms as associated with PTSD, some people may develop more severe symptoms associated with CPTSD. An important consideration in healing from CPTSD is to engage in self-care. Self-care is more than simple acts of getting enough sleep, especially when symptoms of CPTSD are affecting the quality of your life. Here are several tips to help ensure that your self-care is centered on helping you heal and re-engage in life.

Awareness. Becoming aware of what your body is telling you is important in learning to create a self-care program that is geared to your specific needs. For example, recognizing if you are feeling run-down, unusually tired, anxious, or depressed can help you with changing your sleep schedule, or taking a break when needed. Awareness can include recognizing if you are experiencing symptoms such as mental fog, exhaustion, physical limitations, or basically anything that negatively impacts your daily life. By becoming more aware of your mind/body/emotion's connection, you can empower yourself in your self-care.

Keep a journal nearby so you can jot down your thoughts, feelings, or body sensations as you are having them, along with the time of day and what you are doing.

Meditation. Because intrusive thoughts, flashbacks, and anxiety are commonly experienced with C-PTSD, meditation can be an excellent way to help self-calm and redirect your energy. Research suggests that meditation and mindfulness techniques are often safe practices, and can be especially useful in conjunction with therapeutic intervention (Cloitre, et al., 2011).

Social Support. Social support may include close friends, family, a significant other, or a trusted counselor or therapist who can help provide emotional support for you along your self-care journey. Social isolation is commonly reported in people with C-PTSD, because sufferers often struggle with public places, noise, or emotional triggers. Symptoms can be challenging for those battling C-PTSD, so having someone to talk to for encouragement, guidance, or just a shoulder to lean on is important in helping with healing.

Consistency. Consistency is about sticking to a routine, which should include daily tasks such as getting quality sleep each night, taking care of personal hygiene, eating a healthy diet, drinking plenty of water, and keeping a schedule of daily chores. People coping with the effects of C-PTSD often struggle with simple tasks such as getting out of bed because of the emotional and physical exhaustion that often accompanies them. Having a daily schedule is important for healing and re-engaging back in life. *Tip:* Jot down a daily schedule starting with simple tasks (showering, making your bed) and consider building one new task daily or weekly, according to recommendations/thoughts.

Counseling. When you are considering seeking a Counselor think about your comfort with the person as well as his or her qualifications and experience treating C-PTSD & PTSD. Keep in mind the importance of evidence-based, trauma-focused treatments like Cognitive Processing Therapy (CPT), Prolonged Exposure (PE), and Eye Movement Desensitization and Reprocessing (EMDR). When a therapist has experience in trauma-treatment they will talk about safety from the beginning (physical safety, emotional safety) and creating a safe environment where healing can occur. They will talk about self-care, boundaries, grounding, and resources. Their approach recognizes that your behavior isn't *who* you are—rather that it makes sense based on your history. It is what happened to you, not who you are! They work to understand the coping skills you have utilized that have not been effective, how you survived your experiences, and help you build new healthy coping skills. They move at a pace you're comfortable with, collaborating with you along the way, and work to keep you within your window of tolerance of emotions.

Medication. C-PTSD is still a relatively new condition, so some may not be as aware of it. This can make it hard to get an official diagnosis, and you might be diagnosed with PTSD instead of C-

PTSD. There's no specific test for determining whether you have C-PTSD, but keeping a detailed log of your symptoms can help your doctor make a more accurate diagnosis. Try to keep track of when your symptoms started as well as any changes in them over time. Medications traditionally used to treat depression can also help with symptoms of CPTSD. However this much be discussed with your medical provider. Medication tends to work best when combined with another form of Clinical work. If your medical provider is recommending medication, it will be important to continue to work with your them to ensure you obtain the correct medication and dosage. It is not uncommon to try several medications until the correct medication & dosage is found. **Please do not get discouraged! You are worth it!**

Benefits of Mindfulness

Mindfulness improves attention and focus, self-control, emotional resilience and recovery from trauma and addictions, as well it builds empathy skills and enhances memory capabilities.

Attention and Focus – Strengthening our "mental muscle" for bringing focus back to where we want it, when we want it, and it improves attention and learning, and results in better performance.

Emotional Regulation – Observing our emotions helps us recognize when they occur, to see their transient nature, and to change how we respond to them. Mindfulness creates changes in the brain that correspond to less reactivity, and gives us the ability to engage in tasks even more effectively when emotions are activated.

Adaptability – Becoming aware of our patterns enables us to gradually change habitual behaviors.

Calming – Breathing and other mindfulness practices relax the body and mind, giving access to peace independent of external circumstances. It will reduce stress hormones, anxiety, and distress when placed in a stressful social situation.

Resilience – Seeing something objectively reduces the amount of "chatter" we add to the world's natural ups and downs, giving us greater balance. This reduces depression in children, teens, and adults.

Visualization/Guided Imagery

Guided imagery can help to calm your body and simultaneously relax your mind. It's pleasant to practice, and not difficult or intimidating to learn. It can help you to de-stress in minutes, but can also be a useful strategy for maintaining resilience toward stress during difficult times. Guided imagery is a convenient and simple relaxation technique that can help you quickly and easily manage stress and reduce tension in your body. One of the more common techniques is as follows:

Get into a relaxed position, like the one that is used for meditation. Find a position where your physical comfort won't be a distraction.

Use diaphragmic deep breathing with eyes closed, focusing on breathing in peace and breathing out stress. This means letting your belly expand and contract with each breath. If you find your shoulders rising and falling, you are likely carrying tension in your body and not breathing in the most relaxed way. Please take note if this is happening.

Once you reach a relaxed state, begin to envision yourself in the midst of the most relaxing environment you can imagine. For some, this would be floating in the cool, clear waters off a tropical island with relaxing music playing in the background. For others, this might be sitting by a fire in a winter cabin surrounded by snow, deep in the woods, sipping hot cocoa and reading a book or listening to relaxing music.

You may want to remember a time and place when you felt wonderful and relaxed (a "happy place" in your memory), the way you imagine a place you've always wanted to visit or may have already visited.

Focusing on this safe/relaxing place, is like a mindfulness exercise—it takes your mind away from the unsafe thoughts you're experiencing and taking you to a safe place. If your mind begins to wander, just gently bring it back to the relaxing environment.

As you imagine your scene, try to involve all of your senses. What does it look like? How does it feel? What special scents are involved? Do you hear the roar of a fire, the splash of a waterfall, or the sounds of birds? Make your vision so real you can even taste it! (Noticing these details in your daily life is a way to increase your mindfulness, which brings lasting stress management benefits as well.)

Stay here for as long as you like. Enjoy your surroundings and let yourself be far from what stresses you. When you're ready to refocus on the present, begin to count back from ten or twenty, and tell yourself that when you get to one, you will feel serene, relaxed, and alert, and enjoy being in the present. The goal is to return feeling calmer and refreshed and less anxious.

- Breathing Exercise

Breathing is a skill that helps to control one's breathing. Often times breathing becomes rapid during periods of anxiety, hypervigilance, stress, and feelings of being overwhelmed. Deep breathing increases the supply of oxygen to your brain and stimulates the parasympathetic nervous system, which promotes a state of calmness. Deep breathing relieves stress and anxiety due to its physiological effect on the nervous system. As well, deep breathing activates specific neurons that help to regulate blood pressure. The neurons alert the vagus nerve that blood pressure is becoming too high, and the vagus nerve responds by lowering the heart rate. The goal of controlled breathing is to slow erratic breathing to regular, rhythmic abdominal breathing, and to make this kind of breathing automatic. This shift in breathing results in long term changes in the nervous system and helps to manage anxiety symptoms. The steps to assist in controlling one's breathing is as follows (I refer to this technique as the 4/4/4):

1. First Technique. Take deep breaths, in through the nose and blow gently out through the mouth. Breathe from the diaphragm (gut), not from the chest. Repeat as many times as necessary to calm down and re-center.
2. Second breathing technique:
   a) Find a comfortable position either sitting or lying down.
   b) Choose comfortable and loose clothing.
   c) Relax your entire body, arms, legs, and abdomen. Release tension in your chest, shoulders, neck, face, and jaw. Take a long slow breath through your nostril for a count of 4 seconds.
   d) Hold that breath for a count of 4 seconds.

e) Breathe out through the mouth, exhaling for a count of 4 seconds.

f) When breathing out try to exhale as much as possible out of the lungs.

g) Repeat and continue for a few minutes or as long as it may take you to begin to feel the effects of being relaxed and in control of your breathing.

h) Practice and integrate this beathing technique into your daily life, and it will become easier over time.

i) The more you integrate this, the more you automatically start to control your breathing at times of anxiety, stress or feeling overwhelmed.

j) Do not attempt breathing retraining without first discussing this with your physician if you have diabetes, kidney disease, or other disorders which might cause metabolic acidosis. In such cases, breathing may have become rapid to normalize the metabolic acidosis and slowing down your breathing might have adverse effects.

k) It is not uncommon to utilize breathing retraining in conjunction with visualization techniques whereby you visualize yourself being in a relaxing location (beach, mountains, or other setting) and visualizing what you see, feel, hear, smell, and touch.

APPENDIX A

1. Wash your bedding, towels, robes, and curtains. Once you've re-fitted them in their proper place, breathe deeply.
2. Remind yourself that stagnancy and sadness aren't permanent.
3. We all just need a little tumble-dry sometimes.
4. Clear off every surface in your home and wipe them down. Consider this a practice in clearing away mental
5. Change up the layout of your home, even if it's just nudging the couch a little to the left. Disrupt your flow in a positive and proactive way.
6. Clean out your purse or everyday bag.
7. Declutter.
8. Reorganize your closet with this goal: I want to feel joy when I open this door. This isn't a chore that needs to be begrudgingly crossed off your list; it's engaging your creativity to enjoy your daily routines more thoroughly.
9. Wipe the leaves of your houseplants to give them a lovely shine. Place them in the sunshine, and while you're at it, sit in the sunlight with them. Soak it in.
10. Create a meditation corner.
11. Update some of your makeup and beauty products that are expired and recycle or refill old ones if possible.
12. List the tasks that have been weighing on you and get them done, one by one.

13. Dust your home. Underneath the gloom, so much is capable of shining.
14. Recycle your old newspapers, junk mail, magazines.
15. Add a bouquet to your home—you can purchase marked-down blooms at your supermarket, or forage one from flora already on the ground or from a few mindfully selected flowers. Even better? Upcycle old tissue paper into permanent floral fixtures.
16. Organize your finances and create an accessible and sustainable budget. Securing yourself financially, to the best of your ability, can remind you how valuable your time truly is.
17. Light a candle, burn some incense, or turn on an essential oil diffuser. Surround yourself with scents that evoke a memory or set an uplifting mood.
18. Polish your jewelry, clean your makeup brushes, wipe down your mirrors and clean your glasses.
19. Sort through your home library and organize your books by color or genre. Donate the ones you no longer love and consider lending a few favorites to neighbors or friends.
20. Create some art for your walls. Use what you have on hand, tack up some old photos, and decorate your space with what inspires you.
21. Organize your digital photos into folders on iCloud, Google Drive, or even on your desktop. Take your time with the activity reflecting on all your favorite moments and memories

APPENDIX B

Pause whatever it is that you're doing and drink a glass of water. Keep a full water bottle or cup with you at all times.

1. Take three deep breaths (4-4-4 technique-breathe in for 4 seconds, hold for 4 seconds and breathe out for 4 seconds)

2. Brew your morning coffee slowly and then use the used grounds to gently exfoliate your skin during your next shower.

3. Pour boiling water into a heat-safe bowl, add a few drops of eucalyptus oil, and put a towel over it. Carefully bring your face under the towel and enjoy the scent and the sensation of the steam.

4. Adorn your body in your favorite jewelry. No matter how luxurious the pieces are (or aren't), remind yourself that you are worthy of adornment and celebration.

5. Make yourself a fruit platter; cut up apples, peel oranges, wash raspberries and blackberries, make melon balls—whatever's in season, decorate a luxurious tray with delicious and affordable fruits. Indulge in the vibrant flavors of all your favorites.

6. Face any confronting feelings that may arise, embrace them, recognize them, then sleep soundly knowing that you won't have a headache tomorrow.

7. Take <u>five</u>, <u>ten</u>, or <u>fifteen</u> minutes to stretch. Meet yourself wherever your body is—there is no need to set flexibility goals, just to move your body within its limits and enjoy the embodied movement.

8. Practice self-massage—your hands are a great place to start.

9. Stand up and fold forward to get your head below your heart. Cradle your elbows into one another and let your head dangle for a few moments. Or scooch your bum to a wall and rest your legs vertically on the wall while you breathe deeply.

10. Go on a walk, even if it's just around the block (you can <u>try a walking meditation</u>). If you live in a city, do a "stoplight walk," where each time you come to a red light, you take a right turn. There are no stops, and you get to take an unusual and unpredictable route.

11. Give yourself a <u>self-breast exam</u>. Familiarize yourself with what's normal and what isn't normal for your body, checking for lumps, inconsistencies, and points of pain.

12. Don't turn on a morning alarm on days you don't have to wake up early. If you have kids and a support person, let them know that you're taking a morning to sleep in and they're on-duty.

13. Do something physically exerting: break down cardboard boxes for recycling, sprint to the end of the block, jump rope in your driveway. Imagine your stress exhausting itself and leaving your body.

14. Roll out tension using a foam roller, massage balls, or even a tennis ball.

15. Use a homemade sugar scrub to exfoliate your lips, then neatly apply your favorite lip color or balm. Smile in the mirror and tell yourself something lovely, because kindness on our lips is the ultimate topcoat.

16. Get a lotion in your favorite scent. After your next shower, apply it generously and lovingly over every inch of your body.

17. Schedule the appointment that supports your well-being—you can do them all at once, or slowly add to your list throughout the coming weeks. Even if making calls is stressful, give that time as a gift to your future self.

18. Take the medication, the vitamins, the supplements that serve you with consultation with your health care team/physician.

19. Take exactly the type of shower you want to take. Long, short, hot, cold, filled with luxurious products or affordable bar soap; bathe and refresh the body that helps you face the world.

20. During your morning or evening routine, take a few extra moments to brush your hair slowly or massage your scalp.

Brush a few more times than you need to; this, too, can be self-care.

21. Ask for a hug or for physical touch that soothes you from those who know and care about you.

22. Go outside. Let your body decide on the next step once you are outside. Maybe you only get so far as standing in the sunlight. That's enough.

23. Swap coffee for tea, and lots of it. Tea is hydrating and nourishing and can be easier on our stomachs (especially if you opt for herbal).

24. 27.Surround yourself with sensory experiences—smell, sight, taste, touch, sound. Smell, taste, and touch are particularly good at connecting one back with their body.

APPENDIX C

SELF CARE FOR THE MIND

1. Find a quiet space to pray; you don't have to be of a specific religious persuasion to converse with the universe.

2. Spend twenty minutes unfollowing accounts on social media that make you feel less-than. If you can't unfollow, consider muting them—they'll never know! You'll feel lighter afterwards.

3. Learn to meditate, even if it's only ten minutes a day, even if you are not initially comfortable with the practice. Create time and space to just exist and breathe.

4. Make a music playlist of all your favorite songs. Disappear into it, and allow the memories associated with each song to wash over you.

5. Create or join a book club, or a spiritual support and/or discussion group.

6. Take pictures of everything you're grateful for, wherever you are in the moment. Maybe start a private photo album of these pictures to revisit on difficult days or try using Instagram as a gratitude diary.

7. Make yourself a cup of tea and unsubscribe to every unnecessary email list.

8. Enroll in therapy (there are some online/telephonic options).

9. Snuggle your pets. It soothes and relaxes a stressed brain.

10. Create a mood board full of things that speak to you and inspire you.

11. Allow yourself to indulge in a daydream while you're walking, listening to music, cleaning the house. When a strange idea or memory comes to mind, don't push it away. Follow the story.
12. Take an online class via one of the free (and affordable) online education platforms.
13. Organize your Google Drive, desktop, and/or phone home screen. Set your background to an image or quote that inspires and supports you.
14. Set a reminder of a positive affirmation for yourself somewhere in the future—a week, a month, a year from now. (say something like "Hey Siri, remind me in twenty days that everything will be okay.")
15. Update your passwords and keep yourself safe online.
16. Re-read one of your favorite books, re-watch your favorite movie, eat your favorite childhood snacks. Remember what entertainment brought you joy as a kid!
17. Have a park day without your phone (enjoy doing a craft, reading a book of poetry, and bring tasty snacks).
18. Plan something in advance—whether it's the kind of takeout you'll order on Friday, or it's a two-week vacation five years from now. Having something to look forward to can help you stay motivated and optimistic.
19. Practice generosity by donating or volunteering. Whatever it is, do it quietly and intentionally for a cause that is meaningful to you.
20. Engage in some self-directed art therapy.
21. Develop positive affirmations that work for you, and find visible or memorable ways to use them daily.
22. Journal honestly.

23. Write down your biggest aspirations and hope for yourself—the BIGGEST ones, this means no holds barred. No one needs to see this.
24. Write a letter to your younger self. What do you know now that younger you would be amazed by?
25. Handwrite a note to your present self. What is it that you want to remember? Could be that you are worthy and loved.
26. If positive self-talk is difficult for you, consider practicing neutral self-talk. Take the small steps that work for you.
27. Write out your values. What is most important to you, and how can you more deeply prioritize these things in your daily life?
28. Remind yourself of who you are, beyond what you are in relation to others. Maybe you're a parent or a child—but who are you outside of that label?
29. Track your moods for a day, or for several days. Put names to what you're feeling every few hours or so, and reflect on the ways your moods fluctuate, and what impacts them positively or negatively.
30. Text a trusted friend how you're feeling. It's okay to be direct about what you need—a listening ear, a loving word, or tender advice.
31. Forgive someone (when you are ready to do so) in particular if it's yourself.

APPENDIX D

1. I Choose to let go of past hurts (as you go through the healing process)
2. I Love and approve of myself and trust in the process of the life I am in
3. I Let go of Fearing mistakes and failure(s)
4. I Work to heal myself through self-compassion & self-love
5. I Continue to be a work in progress by working to become the very best version of myself each day
6. I Love & Accept myself where I am
7. I know that is o.k. to make mistakes and I am not afraid to make them
8. I am worthy of being happy
9. I Love & accept myself wholeheartedly and unconditionally just as I am.
10. I am calm and in control of how I feel
11. I am doing the best I can at any moment, and that is enough
12. I give myself the gift of unconditional love
13. I am powerful, confident, and capable
14. I Choose to be happy each day
15. I am enough

APPENDIX E

Self-Care Strategies

- Ask your partner to give you a back massage
- Do 5 minutes of deep breathing throughout the day
- Make dinner to music you enjoy
- Journal
- Give someone a Hug
- Take a relaxing Bath
- Choose Healthy food you enjoy
- Make a cup of herbal tea
- Make yourself a green smoothie or juice
- Do something creative you enjoy (gardening, crafting, playing a musical instrument)
- Get a Massage
- Get a facial
- Get a pedicure
- Take yourself on a solo date
- Have coffee with a friend
- Meditate

- Read a book

- Enjoy something sweet without regret

- Try a new exercise class

- Go for a walk/hike

- Listen to music you enjoy

- Drink more water

- Do a puzzle

- Buy yourself flowers

APPENDIX F

Our thoughts control how we feel about and see the world around us. Positive thoughts can lead us to feeling good and negative thoughts can make us feel down. Sometimes our thoughts happen so quickly that we fail to notice them, but they can still affect our mood and feelings. These are call "automatic thoughts".

Oftentimes, our automatic thoughts are negative and irrational. Identifying these negative automatic thoughts and replacing them with new rational thoughts can improve our mood.

Utilize this chart to help you identify negative thoughts and replace them with positive affirmations/thoughts.

Date	Time of Day	Intensity of Thought/feeling (1-10)	Duration of Thought/feeling	Situation (location, people, etc.)	Triggering Event (preceding event)	Emotional Behavioral Initial Reaction (your feelings about the event	New thought/reaction to feeling

APPENDIX G

21 Ways to Help Someone with PTSD

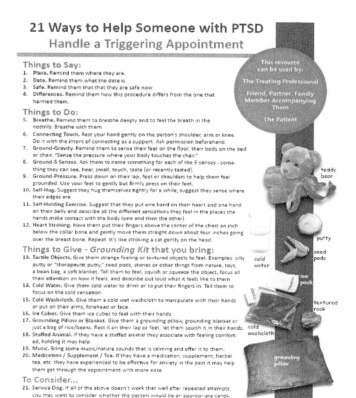

21 Ways to Help Someone with PTSD
Handle a Triggering Appointment

Things to Say:
1. Place. Remind them where they are.
2. Date. Remind them what the date is.
3. Safe. Remind them that that they are safe now
4. Differences. Remind them how this procedure differs from the one that harmed them.

Things to Do:
5. Breathe. Remind them to breathe deeply and to feel the breath in the nostrils. Breathe with them
6. Connecting Touch. Rest your hand gently on the person's shoulder, arm or knee. Do it with the intent of connecting as a support. Ask permission beforehand.
7. Ground-Gravity. Remind them to sense their feet on the floor, their body on the bed or chair. "Sense the pressure where your body touches the chair."
8. Ground-5 Senses. Ask them to name something for each of the 5 senses - something they can see, hear, smell, touch, taste (or recently tasted).
9. Ground-Pressure. Press down on their lap, feet or shoulders to help them feel grounded. Use your feet to gently but firmly press on their feet.
10. Self-Hug. Suggest they hug themselves tightly for a while; suggest they sense where their edges are.
11. Self-Holding Exercise. Suggest that they put one hand on their heart and one hand on their belly and describe all the different sensations they feel in the places the hands make contact with the body (one and then the other)
12. Heart Stroking. Have them put their fingers above the center of the chest an inch below the collar bone and gently move them straight down about four inches going over the breast bone. Repeat. It's like stroking a cat gently on the head.

Things to Give - *Grounding Kit* that you bring:
13. Tactile Objects. Give them strange feeling or textured objects to feel. Examples: silly putty or "therapeutic putty," seed pods, stones or other things from nature, toys, a bean bag, a soft blanket. Tell them to feel, squish or squeeze the object, focus all their attention on how it feels, and describe out loud what it feels like to them
14. Cold Water. Give them cold water to drink or to put their fingers in. Tell them to focus on the cold sensation.
15. Cold Washcloth. Give them a cold wet washcloth to manipulate with their hands or put on their arms, forehead or face.
16. Ice Cubes. Give them ice cubes to feel with their hands
17. Grounding Pillow or Blanket. Give them a grounding pillow, grounding blanket or just a bag of rice/beans. Rest it on their lap or feet, let them squish it in their hands.
18. Stuffed Animal. If they have a stuffed animal they associate with feeling comforted, holding it may help.
19. Music. Bring some music/nature sounds that is calming and offer it to them.
20. Medication / Supplement / Tea. If they have a medication, supplement, herbal tea, etc. they have experienced to be effective for anxiety in the past it may help them get through the appointment with more ease.

To Consider...
21. Service Dog. If all of the above doesn't work that well after repeated attempts, you may want to consider whether the person would be an appropriate candidate for a service dog

This resource can be used by:
The Treating Professional
Friend, Partner, Family Member Accompanying Them
The Patient

teddy bear
putty
seed pods
cold water
ice pack
textured rock
cold washcloth
grounding pillow

APPENDIX H

THE 4F TRAUMA PERSONALITY TYPES

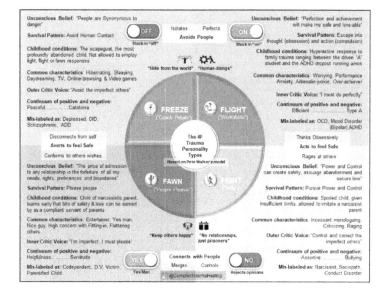

APPENDIX I

Each type of trauma counts as one. If a person who's been physically abused, with one alcoholic parent, and a mother who was beaten up has an ACE score of three. The most important thing to remember is that the ACE score is meant as a guideline: If you experienced other types of toxic stress over months or years, then those would likely increase your risk of health consequences, depending on the positive childhood experiences you had **prior** to your 18th birthday:

1. Did a parent or other adult in the household often or very often... Swear at you, insult you, put you down, or humiliate you? or Act in a way that made you afraid that you might be physically hurt?

   No___If Yes, enter 1 __

2. Did a parent or other adult in the household often or very often... Push, grab, slap, or throw something at you? or Ever hit you so hard that you had marks or were injured?

   No___If Yes, enter 1 __

3. Did an adult or person at least 5 years older than you ever... Touch or fondle you or have you touch their body in a sexual way? or Attempt or actually have oral, anal, or vaginal intercourse with you?

   No___If Yes, enter 1 __

4. Did you often or very often feel that … No one in your family loved you or thought you were important or special? or Your family didn't look out for each other, feel close to each other, or support each other?

   No___If Yes, enter 1 __

5. Did you often or very often feel that … You didn't have enough to eat, had to wear dirty clothes, and had no one to protect you? or Your parents were too drunk or high to take care of you or take you to the doctor if you needed it?

   No___If Yes, enter 1 __

6. Were your parents ever separated or divorced?

   No___If Yes, enter 1 __

7. Was your mother or stepmother:

   No ___ If Yes, enter 1_____

8. Often or very often pushed, grabbed, slapped, or had something thrown at her? or Sometimes, often, or very often kicked, bitten, hit with a fist, or hit with something hard? or Ever repeatedly hit over at least a few minutes or threatened with a gun or knife?
   No___If Yes, enter 1 __

9. Did you live with anyone who was a problem drinker or alcoholic, or who used street drugs?

   No___If Yes, enter 1 __

10. Was a household member depressed or mentally ill, or did a household member attempt suicide?

No___If Yes, enter 1 __

11. Did a household member go to prison?

No___If Yes, enter 1 __

Now add up your "Yes" answers: _ This is your ACE Score

Appendix J

Name: _____

Today's Date: _____

Indicate for each of the statements below the degree to which this change occurred in your life as a result of the crisis/disaster, using the following scale.

0   = *I did not experience this change as a result of my crisis.*

1   = *I experienced this change to a very small degree as a result of my crisis.*

2   = *I experienced this change to a small degree as a result of my crisis.*

3   = *I experienced this change to a moderate degree as a result of my crisis.*

4   = *I experienced this change to a great degree as a result of my crisis.*

5   = *I experienced this change to a very great degree as a result of my crisis.*

Possible Areas of Growth and Change	0	1	2	3	4	5
1. I changed my priorities about what is important in life.						
2. I have a greater appreciation for the value of my own life.						
3. I developed new interests.						
4. I have a greater feeling of self-reliance.						
5. I have a better understanding of spiritual matters.						
6. I more clearly see that I can count on people in times of trouble.						
7. I established a new path for my life.						
8. I have a greater sense of closeness with others.						
9. I am more willing to express my emotions.						
10. I know better that I can handle difficulties.						
11. I am able to do better things with my life.						
12. I am better able to accept the way things work out.						
13. I can better appreciate each day.						
14. New opportunities are available which wouldn't have been otherwise.						
15. I have more compassion for others.						
16. I put more effort into my relationships.						
17. I am more likely to try to change things which need changing.						
18. I have a stronger religious faith.						

19. I discovered that I'm stronger than I thought I was.					
20. I learned a great deal about how wonderful people are.					
21. I better accept needing others.					

Post Traumatic Growth Inventory Scoring – This is only meant as an opportunity to self-assess where you have been, where you are and what areas you desire to grow. It is not meant to be used in this instance to obtain clinical results/information.

APPENDIX K

The International Trauma Questionnaire (ITQ)

Instructions: Please identify the experience that troubles you most and answer the questions in relation to this experience.

Brief description of the experience

_____

When did the experience occur? (circle one)

a.   less than 6 months ago
b.   to 12 months ago
c.   to 5 years ago
d.   5 to 10 years ago
e.   to 20 years ago
f.   more than 20 years ago

Below are a number of problems that people sometimes report in response to traumatic or stressful life events. Please read each item carefully, then circle one of the numbers to the right to indicate how much you have been bothered by that problem <u>in the past month</u>.

Not A little Moderately Quite Extremely at all bit a bit

P1. Having upsetting dreams that replay part of the experience or are clearly related to the experience?	0	1	2	3	4
P2. Having powerful images or memories that sometimes come into your mind in which you feel the experience is happening again in the here and now?	0	1	2	3	4
P3. Avoiding internal reminders of the experience (for example, thoughts, feelings, or physical sensations)?	0	1	2	3	4
P4. Avoiding external reminders of the experience (for example, people, places, conversations, objects, activities, or situations)?	0	1	2	3	4
P5. Being "super-alert", watchful, or on guard?	0	1	2	3	4
P6. Feeling jumpy or easily startled?	0	1	2	3	4

In the past month have the above problems:

P7. Affected your relationships or social life?	0	1	2	3	4
P8. Affected your work or ability to work?	0	1	2	3	4
P9. Affected any other important part of your life such as parenting, or school or college work, or other important activities?	0	1	2	3	4

Cloitre et al. (2018) *Acta Psychiatrica Scandinavica.* 10.1111/acps.

Below are problems that people who have had stressful or traumatic events sometimes experience. The questions refer to ways you typically feel, ways you typically think about yourself and ways you typically relate to others. Answer the following, thinking about how true each statement is of you.

How true is this of you?

C1. When I am upset, it takes me a long time to calm down.	0	1	2	3	4
C2. I feel numb or emotionally shut down.	0	1	2	3	4
C3. I feel like a failure.	0	1	2	3	4
C4. I feel worthless.	0	1	2	3	4
C5. I feel distant or cut off from people.	0	1	2	3	4
C6. I find it hard to stay emotionally close to people.	0	1	2	3	4
C7. Created concern or distress about your relationships or social life?	0	1	2	3	4
C8. Affected your work or ability to work?	0	1	2	3	4
C9. Affected any other important parts of your life such as parenting, or school or college work, or other important activities?	0	1	2	3	4

Cloitre et al. (2018) *Acta Psychiatrica Scandinavica*. DOI: 10.1111/acps.12956

Numerous studies are currently taking place around the world as part of the standardization process of the *International Trauma Questionnaire (ITQ)* used to assess the core features of both C-PTSD and PTSD. The ITQ has been used, or is currently in use, in 29 countries across six continents. Preliminary evidence suggests that the ITQ is an instrument that produces reliable and valid scores and can adequately distinguish between PTSD and C-PTSD cross-culturally. Simply provided as an example of questions that are considered when working with clients.

APPENDIX L

Abreaction – The discharge of emotion involved in recalling an event that has been repressed because it was consciously intolerable.

Acting out – Originally an analytic term referring to the expression of unconscious feelings about a therapist or other authority figures

Affect – A pattern of observable behaviors that is the expression of a subjectively experienced feeling state (emotion).

Anniversary reaction – The experience of reacting with feelings or behavior on the "anniversary" of a previous event.

Amygdala – The amygdala is a small region of the brain that plays a key role in emotional regulation, emotional memory, and responses to emotional stimuli.

Attachment – The term "attachment" refers to a lasting, emotional/psychological bond that is forged between people.

Body Memory – The term refers to body sensations that symbolically or literally captures some aspect of the trauma

Boundaries – Guidelines, rules, or limits that a person creates to identify for themselves what are reasonable, safe, and permissible ways for other people to behave around them, and how they will respond when someone steps outside those limits.

Childhood Abuse and Neglect – Childhood abuse and neglect refer to emotional/sexual abuse/physical abuse perpetrated when a person is a child or teen.

Codependency – a relationship in which an otherwise mentally healthy person is controlled or manipulated by another who is affected by an addiction or mental illness.

Cognitive-Behavioral Therapy (CBT) – A structured form of therapy based on the belief that thoughts, not outside circumstances, control our feelings and behaviors, and that our feelings and behaviors are consequently under our own control.

Complex Post-Traumatic Stress Disorder – A psychological injury that results from prolonged exposure to social or interpersonal trauma, disempowerment, captivity, or entrapment, with lack or loss of a viable escape route for the victim.

Countertransference – A therapist's conscious or unconscious emotional reactions to a client. It is a therapist's job to monitor his or her reactions to a client and to minimize their impact on the therapeutic relationship and treatment.

Cortisol – Cortisol is a stress hormone that is secreted by the adrenal glands and converts protein into energy. When a person feels unsafe or threatened in some manner, the amygdala signals the endocrine system which releases cortisol and causes an increased heart rate and a rise in blood pressure in preparation for a defensive response such as fight or fright.

Denial – The practice of believing or imagining that some painful or traumatic circumstance, event or memory does not exist or did not happen.

Dependency – An inappropriate and chronic reliance by an adult individual on another individual for their health, subsistence, decision making or personal and emotional well-being.

Depersonalization/Derealization – This is one of a number of symptoms of C-PTSD and is a form of dissociation in which a person feels as though they are not real, that they are disconnected from themselves, and are somewhat distant or detached from what is happening to them.

Dialectic Behavioral Therapy (DBT) – DBT is a psychosocial treatment developed for patients with borderline personality disorder which combines intensive individual and group therapy.

Dissociation– Dissociation is a central feature of C-PTSD, when one or more parts of the person's psyche becomes fixated on avoiding and/or defending the self from the painful emotions of re-experiencing the trauma.

Dopamine – Dopamine acts as a neurotransmitter in the brain. Increased levels of the neurotransmitters—serotonin, norepinephrine, and dopamine—has been found to reduce depression.

Dual Diagnosis – This refers to the co-existence of a mental disorder and substance abuse disorder.

EMDR – Eye Movement Desensitization and Reprocessing (EMDR), a psychological technique sometimes used in the treatment of post-traumatic stress disorder (PTSD).

Emotional Abuse – Any pattern of behavior directed at one individual by another which causes the recipient to develop a destructive sense of fear, obligation, or guilt.

Emotional Flashbacks – Emotional flashbacks (EFs) are one of the most common symptoms of C-PTSD, and involve mild to intense feeling states that were felt in past trauma and are layered over present-day situations.

Enabling – A pattern of behavior, often adopted by abuse victims, which seeks to avoid confrontation and conflict by absorbing the abuse without challenging it or setting boundaries.

Family of Choice (FOC) – The family a person chooses to be with.

Family of Origin (FOO) – The family that a person was born in or raised in.

Fawn Response – As described by Peter Walker, the "fawn" response is one of four defensive reactions to ongoing trauma. Those who fawn tend to put the needs and wants of others ahead of their own at the cost of the health of their own egos, and the protection of and compassion for themselves.

Fear of Abandonment – An irrational belief that one is in imminent danger of being personally rejected, discarded, or replaced.

Fight Response – As described by Peter Walker, the "fight" response is one of four defensive reactions to ongoing trauma. Those with C-PTSD who have a fight response tend to react with anger and contempt.

Flight Response – As described by Peter Walker, the "flight" response is one of four defensive reactions to ongoing trauma. Those with C-PTSD who engage in a flight response, try to move away from and distract themselves from their feelings.

Freeze Response – As described by Peter Walker, the "freeze" response is one of four defensive reactions to ongoing trauma. Those with C-PTSD who use a freeze response often isolate themselves from others to dissociate or distance themselves from their pain and fear.

Gaslighting – The practice of brainwashing or convincing a mentally healthy individual that they are going insane, or that their understanding of reality is mistaken or false.

Harassment – Any sustained or chronic pattern of unwelcome behavior by one individual towards another.

Hypervigilance – This refers to the tendency to constantly scan the environment for threats.

Iatrogenesis – When a medical treatment or psychotherapy causes an illness or aggravates an existing illness. In psychotherapy, this may occur as a result of the comments, questions, or attitudes of the therapist.

Identity Disturbance – A psychological term used to describe a distorted or inconsistent self-view.

Impulsiveness – The tendency to act or speak based on current feelings rather than logical reasoning.

Intermittent Reinforcement – when rules, reward or personal boundaries are handed out or enforced inconsistently and occasionally.

Intimidation – Any form of veiled, hidden, indirect or non-verbal threat.

Invalidation – The creation or promotion of an environment which encourages an individual to believe that their thoughts, beliefs, values, or physical presence are inferior, flawed, problematic or worthless.

Low Self-Esteem – A common name for a negatively distorted self-view which is inconsistent with reality.

Manipulation – The practice of steering an individual into a desired behavior for the purpose of achieving a hidden personal goal.

Minimization – To downplay, belittle, trivialize, or discount another person's (or your own) feelings, thoughts, or opinions.

Narcissist– A person who behaves with a pattern of selfishness, grandiosity, need for admiration, self-focus and a lack of empathy or consideration toward others.

Neglect – A passive form of abuse in which the physical or emotional needs of a dependent are disregarded or ignored by the person responsible for them.

Normalizing – This is a tactic used to desensitize an individual to abusive, coercive, or inappropriate behaviors.

"Not My Fault Syndrome" – The practice of avoiding personal responsibility for one's own words and actions.

Numbing – A symptom common to individuals with C-PTSD. It represents an individual's attempt to compensate for intrusive thoughts, memories, or feelings of the trauma by shutting down and becoming numb to internal or external stimuli.

Physical Abuse – Any form of voluntary behavior by one individual which inflicts pain, disease, or discomfort on another, or deprives them of necessary health, nutrition, and comfort.

Reparenting – First termed by Pete Walker (2013), reparenting describes the process of serving as one's own parents to heal from the attachment disorder which commonly develops in C-PTSD.

Repression – An unconscious defense mechanism that occurs when unacceptable ideas, images, or fantasies are kept out of awareness.

Revictimization – This describes the experience of a survivor being victimized or traumatized after the occurrence of the original trauma.

Sense of Entitlement – An unrealistic, unmerited, or inappropriate expectation of favorable living conditions and favorable treatment at the hands of others.

Serotonin – It acts as a neurotransmitter in the brain. Increased levels of the neurotransmitters— serotonin, norepinephrine, and dopamine—have been found to reduce depression.

Shaming – The difference between blaming and shaming is that blaming someone tells you that you *did* something bad, in shaming someone tells you that you *are* bad.

Silent Treatment – A passive-aggressive form of emotional abuse in which displeasure, disapproval, and contempt are exhibited through nonverbal gestures while maintaining verbal silence.

Sleep Deprivation – The practice of routinely interrupting, impeding, or restricting another person's sleep cycle.

Social Anxiety Disorder – A mental health condition where a person becomes anxious when faced with interacting in social situations

Toxic Shame – Refers to a belief that you are an inferior and/or unlovable person. Shame is something everyone experiences from time to time when we make an error; toxic shame is the belief that *you* are the error.

Trauma – An event or experience that is deeply disturbing on an emotional or psychological level.

Trauma-Informed Care – An organizational structure and treatment framework that involves understanding, recognizing, and responding to the effects of all types of trauma. Trauma-informed care also emphasizes physical, psychological, and emotional safety for both consumers and providers, and helps survivors rebuild a sense of control and empowerment.

Trauma Response – Peter Walker outlines four basic defenses that most people use in life, but a sufferer of C-PTSD becomes fixated and maladaptive due to ongoing trauma. These defenses include fight, flight, freeze and fawn.

Trigger – It is a stimulus such as a smell, sound, or sight that triggers feelings of trauma.

Vicarious Traumatization– Sometimes called compassion fatigue, it is the latest term that describes the phenomenon generally associated with the "cost of caring" for others (Figley, 1982).

APPENDIX M

A Practical Guide to Complex PTSD: Compassionate Strategies to Begin Healing from Childhood Trauma by Arielle Schwartz PhD

Childhood Disrupted: How Your Biography Becomes Your Biology, and How You Can Heal by Donna Jackson Nakazawa

Complex PTSD: From Surviving to Thriving: A Guide and Map for Recovering from Childhood Trauma by Pete Walker

Complex PTSD Trauma and Recovery: Learn How Trauma Affects Self-Esteem and the Strategies for Dealing with PTSD Symptoms, Regaining Emotional Balance, and Control of Your Life by Elise Van der Kolk and Erica Olsen

Eye Movement Desensitization and Reprocessing (EMDR) Therapy, Third Edition: Basic Principles, Protocols, and Procedures by Francine Shapiro

From Generation to Generation: Healing Intergenerational Trauma Through Storytelling by Emily Wanderer Cohen

Harris, M. & Fallot, R. D. (Eds.) (2001). *Using Trauma Theory to Design Service Systems. New Directions for Mental Health Services.* San Francisco: Jossey-Bass.

Healing Developmental Trauma: How Early Trauma Affects Self-Regulation, Self-Image, and the Capacity for Relationship by Laurence Heller Ph.D. and Aline LaPierre Psy.D.

Healing from Trauma: A Survivor's Guide to Understanding Your Symptoms and Reclaiming Your Life by Jasmin Lee Cori and Robert Scaer

Healing Trauma: A Pioneering Program for Restoring the Wisdom of Your Body by Peter A. Levine Ph.D.

In an Unspoken Voice: How the Body Releases Trauma and Restores Goodness by Peter A. Levine (Author), Gabor Mate (Foreword)

It Didn't Start with You: How Inherited Family Trauma Shapes Who We Are and How to End the Cycle by Mark Wolynn

It's not me: Understanding Complex Trauma, Attachment and Dissociation by Anabel Gonzalez

Jennings, A. (2015). Retraumatization [PowerPoint slides]. Retrieved from http://theannainstitute.org

My Grandmother's Hands: Racialized Trauma and the Pathway to Mending Our Hearts and Bodies by Resmaa Menakem, MSW LICSW SEP, Cary Hite, et al

The Body Keeps the Score: Brain, Mind, and Body in the Healing of Trauma by Bessel van der Kolk M.D

In an Unspoken Voice: How the Body Releases Trauma and Restores Goodness by Peter A. Levine Ph.D., Ed Nash, et al.

Waking the Tiger: Healing Trauma by Peter A. Levine and Ann Frederick

Seeking Safety: A Treatment Manual for PTSD and Substance Abuse, Najavitis LM.

Retrain Your Brain (Cognitive Behavioral Therapy in 7 Weeks: A Workbook for Managing Depression and Anxiety) by Seth J. Gillihan

The Boy Who Was Raised as a Dog: And Other Stories from a Child Psychiatrist's Notebook -- What Traumatized Children Can Teach Us About Loss, Love, and Healing by Bruce D. Perry, Maia Szalavitz, et al.

The Complex PTSD Workbook: A Mind-Body Approach to Regaining Emotional Control and Becoming Whole by Arielle Schwartz

Treatment of Complex Trauma: A Sequenced, Relationship-Based Approach by Christine A. Courtois_, Julian D. Ford, et al.

Trauma and Recovery: The Aftermath of Violence--From Domestic Abuse to Political Terror by Judith Lewis Herman

Trauma Treatment Toolbox: 165 Brain-Changing Tips, Tools & Handouts to Move Therapy Forward by Jennifer Sweeton

The Posttraumatic Growth Workbook: Coming Through Trauma Wiser, Stronger, and More Resilient by Richard G Tedeschi PhD et al.

When the Body Says No: Exploring the Stress-Disease Connection by Gabor Maté, Daniel Maté, et al

The Body Keeps the Score by Bessel Van der Kolk

When Pleasing You is Killing Me by Les Carter.

Codependent No More by Melody Beattie.

Healing Trauma by Peter Levine.

Waking the Tiger: Healing Trauma by Peter Levine.

Complex PTSD: From Surviving to Thriving by

Appendix N

- Recovery International
- Adult Children of Alcoholics
- Al-Anon/Alateen
- Alcoholics Anonymous
- AlcoholScreening.org
- Alzheimer's Association
- American Association of Retired Persons Grief and Loss Information
- American Association of Suicidology: Support for family/friends that have lost a loved one to suicide
- Anxiety and Depression Association of America, Anxiety and Depression Association of America peer-to-peer support group
- Attention Deficit Disorder Association
- Autism Society of America
- The Balanced Mind Foundation
- Brain Injury Association of America
- Caregiver Action Network
- Children and Adults with Attention Deficit/Hyperactivity Disorder (CHADD) In addition to support groups,

CHADD has a section for parents which includes many helpful resources (look at list of options on right-hand side of the page) and a link that explains their Parent to Parent Family Training classes. For more information about these on-line training classes, review the information at the link we've provided or contact the CHADD national resource center at 1-800-233-4050.

- Co-Dependents Anonymous or sign up for their email list. You can also visit http://www.codependents.org/

- The Compassionate Friends Grief Support: After the death of a child (Use this link to find groups in your area)

- CoSLAA Support groups for family and friends of people who have a sex addiction

- Crisis Text Line

- Debtors Anonymous

- Depression and Bipolar Support Alliance

- Dual Diagnosis of Oregon, Inc. (Although based in Oregon, offer support to those in other areas who wish to establish groups to help those who have both a mental health and alcohol/substance abuse condition)

- Dual Recovery Anonymous: Support for those who have both a mental health and alcohol/substance abuse condition

- Emotions Anonymous: Modeled after the Alcoholics Anonymous 12-step program, Emotions Anonymous is open to any individual dealing with emotional difficulties.

- Federation of Families for Children's Mental Health, a parent support and advocacy network

- Freedom from Fear (In addition to finding support groups, you can use the Finding Help/Resources tab on left hand side to access on-line support, e-mail support, and blogs)

- Gamblers Anonymous

- Gift from Within: Article for partners (Support for both men and women with post-traumatic stress disorder. Use the Trauma Support tab at the top of the page to access a wide variety of support options.)

- Hospice Foundation of America (Grief and Loss section includes link to find a local hospice office using link from left-hand side of the page; many offices offer grief support groups. National hospice office can be reached by calling 1-800-868-5171.)

- International Obsessive Compulsive Disorder Foundation

- International Society for the Study of Trauma and Dissociation

- Male Survivor (Discussion board and chat room for men who have been sexually abused can be accessed from Survivors tab on left hand side of the page)

- Narcotics Anonymous

- The National Alliance on Mental Illness (NAMI): A family support and advocacy organization

- National Eating Disorders Association

- O.A.S.I.S.@MAAP (Autism and Asperger Syndrome support group information for both individuals and their family/friends; Support groups tab accessible from left-hand side of the page)

- Overeaters Anonymous Offer in-person, telephone, and on-line meetings

- Parents, Families and Friends of Lesbians and Gays (PFLAG)

- Postpartum Support International and link to support resources in your area (National 24-hour Postpartum Depression Helpline 1.800.944.4PPD)

- S-Anon International Family Groups Support groups for family and friends of people who have a sex addiction

- Self-Mutilators Anonymous

- Sex Addicts Anonymous (description of organization) and find a meeting link http://www.sexaa.org/Meetings/UnitedStates/

- Sidran Institute (Extensive information and resources on ptsd, dissociative disorder, trauma, and self-injury; e-mail or call 1-888-825-8249 to request support group information)

- Survivors of Incest Anonymous (Use the SIA Groups and Intergroups options on the left-hand side of the home page to find meeting information)

- The Arc (Support and information for people with mental retardation and related developmental disabilities and their families) To find a chapter near click here.

- Tourette Syndrome Association, Inc.

- TARA Association for Personality Disorder: National Borderline Personality Disorder Resource and Referral Center

- The TLC Foundation for Body-Focused Repetitive Behaviors

- Well Spouse Association Support for spousal caregivers.

- Witness Justice (Information, resources, and on-line support for victims of violence or trauma, their family and friends, and professionals.

- "After an Attempt" A practical guide developed for individuals who have attempted suicide, their family/friends, and for mental health professionals.

- Air Compassion for Veterans for injured veteran's ongoing healing process.

- American Association of Caregiving Youth gives support to individuals under 18 years of age who are caregivers.

- American Foundation for Suicide Prevention has chapters around the country and offers a variety of information and support resources for those who have lost a loved one to suicide.

- ARCH National Respite Network

- Armed Services YMCA

- ATTACh at 866-453-8224 (Association for Treatment and Training in the Attachment of Children)

- Behavioral Tech, LLC (Information and resources for people with borderline personality disorder and their friends and family)

- Brain and Behavior Research Foundation (formerly known as NARSAD, has information about schizophrenia and depression for individuals and their families)

- Borderline Personality Disorder Resource Center

- Cause USA Comfort for America's Uniformed Services (help for those wounded in military service)

- Families for Depression Awareness (Information about depression and bipolar disorder including how to help someone who is depressed seek treatment and manage treatment, information for friends and family members about taking care of themselves, downloadable Wellness Guides, as well as free brochures including "Helping Someone Who Is Depressed")

- Gateway to PTSD Information

- Geriatric Mental Health Foundation offers information on caregiving, mental health topics relating to older adults, and a Depression Recovery Toolkit.

- GLBT National Help Center at 1-888-843-4564 (adults) and 1-800-246-7743 (adolescents) Provides telephone and e-mail peer counseling as well as information and resources.

- Hazelden offers a helpful question and answers section for friends and family members who care about someone who has an alcohol or substance abuse problem. They also offer an extensive separate website that focuses on co-occurring disorders (when someone has both a mental health condition and an alcohol or substance abuse condition)

- Job Accommodation Network (JAN) is a service provided by the U.S. Department of Labor's Office of Disability Employment Policy. JAN's mission is to facilitate the employment and retention of workers with disabilities by providing employers, employment providers, people with disabilities, their family members, and other interested parties with information on job accommodations, entrepreneurship, and related subjects.

- National Center for PTSD offers "Returning from the War Zone: A Guide for Families of Military Personnel"

- National Center for Trauma Informed Care (NCTIC)

- National Child Traumatic Stress Network

- National Domestic Violence Hotline 1-800-799-SAFE (7233) and 1-800-787-3224 (TTY)

- National Education Alliance for Borderline Personality Disorder 914-835-9011

- S.A.F.E. Alternatives (Information and resources for help with self-injury)

- Schizophrenia.com

- Self-Inflicted Violence (Website includes link to sample newsletter The Cutting Edge)

- Suicide Prevention Resource Center

- Survivors Art Foundation (For trauma survivors)

- U.S. Vets (A non-profit organization that helps homeless veterans access mental health and substance abuse services along with housing and other community supports to achieve successful reintegration into the community.)

- Yellow Ribbon offers information and resources about suicide prevention for teens, parents, and others. Has chapters in many states and some other countries as well as support resources for those who have lost a loved one to suicide.

APPENDIX O

Journal of Alternative and Complementary Medicine |

Trauma-Sensitive Yoga for Post-Traumatic Stress Disorder in Women veterans Who Experienced Military Sexual Trauma

Complementary Therapies in Clinical Practice |

Trauma-informed approaches to physical activity - A scoping study

Psychological Trauma: Theory, Research, Practice, and Policy | Moderators of Treatment Efficacy in a Randomized Controlled Trial of Trauma-Sensitive Yoga as an Adjunctive Treatment for Post-traumatic Stress Disorder

WestCASA | Body Based Therapy for sexual assault survivors

Journal of Trauma & Dissociation |

Mindfulness and yoga for psychological trauma: systematic review and meta-analysis

Dissertation by Rowan Silverberg | TCTSY in peer support groups for survivors of sexual violence

American Psychological Association |

Trauma-Sensitive Yoga as an Adjunctive Mental Health Treatment for Survivors of Intimate Partner Violence: A Qualitative Examination

American Psychological Association |

Yoga as an Intervention for Psychological Symptoms Following Trauma: A Systematic Review and Quantitative Synthesis

Evan Alyse Bodine's Dissertation |

The Lived Experience of Teaching Trauma-Sensitive Yoga: A dissertation by Evan Alyse Bodine

International Journal of Yoga Therapy | Bridging Body and Mind: Considerations for Trauma-Informed Yoga

Boston Medical Center Psychiatry | Meta-Analysis of yoga for PTSD

European Journal of Trauma & Dissociation |

Yoga for PTSD and the role of interoceptive awareness: A preliminary mixed-methods case series study

International Journal of Stress Management |

Trauma Sensitive Yoga as a Complementary Treatment for Post-Traumatic Stress Disorder: A Qualitative Descriptive Analysis

Journal of Alternative & Complementary Medicine |

Effectiveness of an Extended Yoga Treatment for Women with Chronic Post-Traumatic Stress Disorder

The Center on Poverty and Inequality at Georgetown Law |

Gender and Trauma: Somatic Interventions for Girls in Juvenile Justice: Implications for Policy and Practice

Complementary Therapies in Clinical Practice |

Bending without breaking: A narrative review of trauma-sensitive yoga for women with PTSD

Journal of Alternative & Complementary Medicine |

Yoga for Adult Women with Chronic PTSD: A Long-Term Follow-Up Study

Complementary Therapies in Clinical Practice |

Claiming Peaceful Embodiment Through Yoga in The Aftermath of Trauma

Complementary Therapies in Clinical Practice |

Trauma-sensitive yoga as an adjunct mental health treatment in group therapy for survivors of domestic violence: A feasibility study

Alison Rhodes' Dissertation | Yoga for Traumatic Stress

Journal of Clinical Psychiatry |

Yoga as an Adjunctive Treatment for Post-Traumatic Stress Disorder: A Randomized Controlled Trial *(Core Study Establishing an Evidence Base for TCTSY)*

Jennifer West's Dissertation | Moving to Heal: Women's Experiences of Therapeutic Yoga after Complex Trauma

Journal of the American Psychiatric Nurses Association |

Application of Yoga in Residential Treatment of Traumatized Youth

APPENDIX P

REFERENCES

American Psychiatric Association. (2013). Diagnostic and statistical manual of mental disorders (5th ed.). Washington, DC: Author

Brickel & Associates

Burk Harris, Nadine. The Deepest Well: Healing the Long-Term Effects of Childhood Adversity.

Calhoun & Tedeschi, 1990, Post Traumatic Growth

Chris R Brewin, Marylene Cloitre, Philip Hyland, Mark Shevlin, Andreas Maecker, Richard A Bryant, Asma Humayun, Lynne MN Jones, Ashraf Kagee, Cecile Rousseau, Day Somasundaram, Yuriko Suzuki, Simon Wesseley, Mark van Ommeren, Geoffrey M Reed; A review of current evidence regarding the ICD-11 proposals for diagnosis PTSD and Complex PTSD; 2017 Dec; 58:1-15.

Cloitre, M., et al. (2011). Treatment of complex PTSD: Results of the ISTSS expert clinician survey on best practices. *Journal of Traumatic Stress, 24*(6), 615-627.

Cloitre, Marlene; ICD-11 complex post-traumatic stress disorder: simplifying diagnosis in trauma populations.

Wanderer Cohen, Emily. From Generation to Generation: Healing Intergenerational Trauma through Storytelling.

Cori, Jasmin Lee and Scaer, Robert. Healing from Trauma: A Survivor's Guide to Understanding your Symptoms and Reclaiming Your Life.

Perry, Bruce D. The Boy Who Was Raised as a Dog and other Stories from a Child Psychiatrist's Notebook – What Traumatized Children Can Teach Us About Love and Healing.

Courtois, Christine A. and Ford, Julian D et al. Treatment of Complex Trauma: A Sequenced, Relational Based Approach.

Gillihan, Seth J. Retrain Your Brain (2017): Cognitive Behavioral Therapy in 7 weeks: A Workbook for Managing Depression and Anxiety.

Gonzales, Anabel. It's not me: Understanding Complex Trauma, Attachment and Dissociation.

LeCombe, Suzanne. Social Support: Does shame Matter? Journal of Anxiety Disorders, 47, 106-113.

International Society for Traumatic Stress Study (2013).

Heller, Laurence and LaPierre, Aline. Healing Developmental Trauma: How Early Trauma Affects Self-Regulation, Self-Image, and the Capacity for Relationship.

Herman, Judith (1988). Complex PTSD was needed to describe the symptoms of long-term trauma. Acknowledged by the Department of Veterans Affairs.

Herman, J. L. (1992). Complex PTSD: A syndrome in survivors of prolonged and repeated trauma. *Journal of Traumatic Stress,* 5(3), 377-391.

Jackson Nakazawa, Donna. Childhood Disrupted: How Your Biography Becomes Your Biology, and How You Can Heal.

Lewis Herman, Judith. Trauma and Recovery: The Aftermath of Violence-From Domestic Abuse to Political Terror.

Levine, Peter A. and Frederick Ann. Goodness Waking

Levine, Peter A. and Mate, Gabor (Forward). In an Unspoken Voice: How the Body Released Trauma and Restores Goodness.

Levine, Peter A. Healing Trauma: A Pioneering Program for Restoring the Wisdom of Your Body.

Levine, Peter A. and Van der Kolk, Bessel (Forward). Trauma and Memory: Brain and Body in a Search for the Living Past: A Practical Guide for Understanding and Working with Traumatic Memory.

Mate, Gabor and Mate, Daniel, et al. When the Body Says No: Exploring the Stress-Disease Connection

Menakem, Resmaa. My Grandmother's Hands: Racialized Trauma and the Pathway to Mending Our Hears and Bodies.

MentalHealth.net

Schiraldi, Glenn R. The Post Traumatic Stress Disorder Sourcebook.

Schwartz, Arielle. A Practical Guide to Complex PTSD: Compassionate Strategies to Begin Healing from Childhood Trauma. .

Schwartz, Arielle. The Complex PTSD Workbook: A Mind-Body Approach to Regaining Emotional Control and Becoming Whole.

Schwartz, A. (2016). The Neurobiology of Trauma. Retrieved from: Once upon a time, in a not-so-far-away land, there lived a small child.

Sharpiro, Francine. Eye Movement Desensitization and Reprocessing (EMDR) Therapy, Third Edition: Basic Principles, Protocols and Procedures.

Shapiro, Francine, Maslow, Florence & Maxfield Louise (edited by). The Handbook of EMDR and Family Therapy Processes edited

Siegel, D. (2020) The Developing Mind.

Siegel, D. J. (2011). Mindsight: The new science of personal transformation. New York: Bantam Books Trade Paperbacks.

Siegel, D. & Bryson, T. (2020) The Power of Showing Up.

Simon, N., et al. (2019). Associations between perceived social support, posttraumatic stress disorder (PTSD) and complex PTSD (CPTSD): Implications for treatment. *European Journal of Psychotraumatology, 10,* 1 – 11.

Slepian, M. L., Kirby, J. N., & Kalokerinos, E. K. (2019). Shame, guilt, and secrets on the mind. Emotion.

Slepian, M. L., & Greenaway, K. H. (2018). The benefits and burdens of keeping others' secrets.

Slepian, M. L., Masicampo, E. J., & Galinsky, A. D. (2016). The hidden effects of recalling secrets: Assimilation, contrast, and the burdens of secrecy. Journal of Experimental Psychology: General, 145, 27–48.

Slepian, M. L., Halevy, N., & Galinsky, A. D. (2018). The solitude of secrecy: Thinking about secrets evokes motivational conflict and feelings of fatigue. Personality and Social Psychology Bulletin, 45(7).

Sweeton, Jennifer (forwarded by). Trauma Treatment Toolbox: 165 Brain-Changing Tips, Tools & Handouts to Move Therapy.

Tanasugarn, Annie (2019). The Importance of Self Care when Coping with CPTSD.

TraumaCenter.net

Van der Kolk, Bessel, M.D. The Body Keeps the Score: Brain, Mind, and Body in the Healing of Trauma.

Van de Kolk, Elise, and Olsen, Erica. Complex PTSD Trauma and Recovery: Learn How Trauma Affects Self-Esteem and the Strategies for Dealing with PTSD Symptoms, Regaining Emotional Balance, and Control of Your Life

Walker, Peter. Complex PTSD: From Surviving to Thriving: A Guide and Map for Recovering from Childhood Trauma

Wolyn, Mark. It Didn't Start with You: How Inherited Family Trauma Shapes Who We Are and How to End the Cycle.

Made in the USA
Middletown, DE
16 June 2021